To

THE SATURDAY BOOK

EIGHTEENTH YEAR

G. Severini

THE SATURDAY *BOOK*

18

EDITED BY
JOHN HADFIELD
AND PUBLISHED BY
HUTCHINSON OF LONDON

THE SATURDAY BOOK

was founded in 1941 by Leonard Russell and has been edited since 1952 by John Hadfield. This eighteenth annual issue was made, printed and bound at Watford in Great Britain by Taylor, Garnett Evans & Company, Ltd. The type was set at the Gainsborough Press, St. Albans, by Fisher, Knight & Company, Ltd. The blocks were made at Bromley, Kent, by the Grout Engraving Company, Ltd., and the colour plates were printed by the Anchor Press, Ltd., at Tiptree, Essex.

PUBLISHED IN 1958

THE FRONTISPIECE reproduces a design, 'Serenade à la lune,' by Gino Severini for *Fleurs et Masques*, 1930.

INTRODUCTION

ONE of the features in this number of *The Saturday Book* was to have been an illustrated essay on feathers by Robert Gibbings. It had seemed to us both to be a *Saturdiurnal* subject—beautiful, curious and disregarded. There was also a certain piquancy in a man who weighed some seventeen stone discussing and engraving—with his characteristic finesse and lightness of touch— swansdown and wren's wings.

There is no feature on feathers in this issue, for Robert Gibbings died in January. An Introduction is no occasion for an Obituary—and any thoughts of an obituary nature would have conjured up that irrepressible twinkle in Robert's eyes. But we want his name to appear on our first page because he was not only a regular contributor, he was also, in our view, the epitome of what we like to regard as the *Saturday Book* reader.

The pieces by Robert Gibbings which we have printed in the past few years are an index of his intellectual and aesthetic range—Venetian well-heads, tropical fish, scenes on the Seine, and finally, in last year's issue, some testamentary observations on the craft of which he was a modern master, wood-engraving.

Robert's personality—his verve and volume, his stature and skill —was exceptional. But his mental and aesthetic curiosity, and his taste for the more recondite pleasures of life, were, we like to think, typically *Saturdiurnal* characteristics. He was totally uninterested in politics, careerism, commerce and keeping up with the Joneses. But he loved vintage traction engines and trout, microscopes, boats and birds, fossils, Sibelius, post-Impressionists and Negro dancing, rain, all things Irish, good talk and good jokes, solitude, Montparnasse and Samoa, print, paper, and pubs, flowers, claret and not wearing a tie. Although he was a most conscientious and industrious craftsman it could be said of him that all his days were Saturdays. May the Berkshire clay lie as lightly on his vast bearded frame as the swansdown from Sweet Thames that he was going to draw for us.

J. H.

CONTENTS

PERSONAL

CURIOUS

WHO's that knocking on the window,
Who's that standing at the door,
What are all those presents
Lying on the kitchen floor ?

Who is the smiling stranger
With hair as white as gin,
What is he doing with the children
And who could have let him in ?

Why has he rubies on his fingers,
A cold, cold crown on his head,
Why, when he caws his carol,
Does the salty snow run red ?

Why does he ferry my fireside
As a spider on a thread,
His fingers made of fuses
And his tongue of gingerbread ?

Why does the world before him
Melt in a million suns,
Why do his yellow, yearning eyes
Burn like saffron buns ?

Watch where he comes walking
Out of the Christmas flame,
Dancing, double-talking :

Herod is his name.

CHARLES CAUSLEY

THE HOLLY & THE THORN
by PETER TOWRY

BEFORE MORNING roll-call, Major Jervas went out of the camp gates, and up hill to the Japanese quarters. It was still dark, but the darkness thinning, and the air very crisp. As he passed the Japanese cookhouse, the smell of cooking pork stopped him, and for a moment he lingered, a lover doting in the wakes of the beloved. Then he went on to the Interpreter's room. The door was open ; inside, under the bright light, sat the Interpreter, shovelling his breakfast into his mouth with chopsticks, one bare foot cocked on the table. He saw Jervas, and stopped eating.

'Well ?'

Jervas stepped inside, and bowed perfunctorily. 'A man has died.'

The Interpreter looked cross. Jervas told him the details.

The Interpreter sniffed. 'You'll have to have the funeral tomorrow. Can't do today. Not your damn Christmas *and* a funeral on one day. But no work this afternoon—you can tell that to the boys. And tell the cooks to collect some pork from the Nippon cookhouse. And sugar for the canteen later in the morning. O.K. ?'

'Yes. Will there be any mail ?'

The Interpreter frowned. 'You boys don't have an idea what I do for you. I was up till two this morning, censoring . . . O.K. Mail this morning, some time. There's one for you.'

Jervas' heart jumped. He bowed, and turned to go.

'Hey !'

Jervas stopped.

[9]

'Merry Christmas,' said the Interpreter, and smoothed his small moustache and smirked and raised his rice-bowl to his mouth again.

The dawn was clearing fast. From the path down, through the vertical tree-trunks, Jervas saw the diagonals of the bamboo roofs of the prison huts, laced about by the high bamboo fence, all as if afloat in the lingering ground mist. It made a weird, geometrical pattern.

Like a Japanese print, he thought : a ruddy Japanese print.

Over breakfast there was some grumbling, at having to go out and work on the farm, even though only till noon, but generally men were cheerful, warmed by that irrational warmth of optimism that the traditional festivals always kindled. Soon the camp was empty. The Interpreter came down with the mail, and left Jervas to check it. The major acted as administrative officer.

There was quite a batch of mail. And there was indeed a letter for him ; from his wife, Rosemary. It was quite recent, only eight months old : she was well, still in Simla, packing Red Cross parcels, with hardly time to play bridge . . . He turned the page, and the tone changed, hardening into deliberately lapidary phrases of love, shaped with strict but vain restraint to mute the despairing, bereaved intimacies beneath.

He read that page twice, and then swore up and down the hut, until he was composed enough to continue with the checking.

But, as automatically he worked, he dreamed : not of the middle past, the twenty years in the tea plantation above Darjeeling, but farther back, and forward. He was sick of the East, and he yearned forwards and backwards to his native Cotswolds : to a farm, where he would retire, to the slopes of dripping beechwoods above the Stroud valley, and to a small house filled with the furniture that had been his father's, yet which he saw still with the precise, vivid curiosity of a child. The breakfast table, round, shining walnut : the pale silver, worn by generations to an incredible frail elegance, the round dome of the hot-dish—and his wife's face beyond. Rosemary—and perhaps that young nephew of hers, James, whom later on in the morning he would take for a walk up the hill, to that dizzy brink whence the eye soared over three counties, to the blue Welsh hills beyond the Severn. But his dream narrowed, focusing greedily on the dome of the hot-dish ; he saw his own face, blown round and infantile, in the shining curve. Slowly, slowly he raised the lid : underneath, there would be crisp bacon, eggs, mushrooms, sausages . . .

He found himself staring foolishly at a letter in his hand, in a Japanese prisoner-of-war camp, on the island of Formosa ; it was Christmas Day, 1944, and the saliva ran in his mouth. He jerked himself away from the thought of food, and turned the letter over in his hands. It was addressed to the man who had died that night.

Gunner Minton. He had been attached to Jervas' own battery, but the Major knew little of him, for he had been one of those most unfortunate, who had arrived, fresh from England, at Singapore the week before it fell. Jervas knew the externals, and a little of Minton's case-history—newly married, well educated, a student interrupted in his studies ; one of those who should have been commissioned, but who, for some reason undivulged, had backed away. A reserved man, but a good prisoner apparently, uncomplaining, oddly self-sufficient ; about twenty-five. Jervas remembered him as one of the palest of the ghosts who drifted about the camp, admitted even by the Japanese as too ill to work : a gaunt anatomy topped with a flare of yellow hair, scarcely worth a shadow to the sun.

Gunner Minton had been also one of those who had as yet received no mail. And here, after almost three years, was a letter for him. That, Jervas thought, *would* happen ; when the war did end, and peace opened those pearly gates, they'd all be blind or paralysed, or dead.

He was interrupted by one of the doctors, hot on the rumour of mail.

'Doc,' said Jervas, 'what hit Minton ? I thought he was off the D.I. list a long way back.'

'Heart,' said the doctor. 'Got up in the night, and fell down dead. Beri-beri takes 'em like that sometimes. A few steaks last July might have saved him. Those blankety Nips—you heard the Camp Commandant's message of love yesterday ? "Too many prisoners are dying, therefore the doctors must work harder : all beri-beri patients to walk barefoot in the morning dew, a certain cure . . ." '

The working squads came in. Queues of men waited to sign for their letters. The lucky ones, trembling, withdrew to read, until Jervas was left alone. One letter only, unclaimed, lay on the table.

Dinner was treated with ceremony. The vegetable soup swam with little yellow shines of pork fat ; there was rather more than the usual cupful of rice.

'Not bad,' said Jervas' neighbour.

The table began at once to discuss past Christmases—turkey, plum puddings, hams, mince pies, alcohol . . .

'But *I*,' said a soured regular captain, 'should be quite happy with a dish of roast sucking Jap. I said sucking.'

The table roared, and in high humour spoke of the approaching end of the war. The war in Europe, a sentry had as good as said, was over ; the Philippines had fallen ; they would be out in two months . . . Rumour ran amok, until presently the diners dispersed, to re-read their letters, and to sleep.

Jervas was roused by a message from the Interpreter—'says the funeral's to be at four sharp : the Nips can't do it tomorrow ; not to worry about the grave—the blokes dug a spare one last time . . .' Furious, Jervas rose, and set the machinery going : warned the padre, detailed volunteer pall-bearers, informed all huts, made sure a coffin was ready.

At four o'clock, a small party stood on the green patch between the huts and the fence ; eight bearers, the padre in white, and a congregation of fifteen, all changed from their usual motley into the last jealously hoarded remnants of their British uniforms. Stiffly, they stood behind the trestled coffin. The Interpreter arrived with one of the Japanese officers. The party bowed. The service began.

Jervas looked away over the coffin, over the high, dirty yellow-brown fence, to the mountains beyond that fell back in tiers, each range more blue, more remote, against the cold pale sky. The much-used phrases hung like smoke in the air. The Lord hath given and the Lord hath taken away. They sang a hymn, shivering, for the sun was going, the chill rising. Abide with me. Fast falls the eventide.

He watched the coffin sway out of the gate, the priest in front, the two Japanese escorts behind, their bayonets shining. He was glad that he did not have to go : it was a long two miles to that bleak hillside graveyard. Yet, though he did not consider himself a religious man, he was a little shocked by the smallness of the congregation. We've got pretty callous, he thought. An empty loneliness swelled in him, and for consolation he felt for the new letter from Rosemary in his pocket. But it did not help, and the hopeless, frustrated rage, that had torn him when he first read the letter, assailed him again. To be free, to be twenty-five again : never to go near that unsuccessful plantation where he had wasted twenty years : never to go near Malaya, where they had run backwards down the peninsula faster than any army had ever run before—but to live, to live fully, and to love ; to return to his roots, and grow upon them : to work, to beget and raise children : to die, and be continued in his children . . .

At the door of the hut an orderly from the hospital hut stopped him, to give him a bundle. Gunner Minton's effects. For the sake of doing something, Jervas glanced through them : the few tattered clothes, the empty tins for putting things in, in case the Red Cross ever came ; a spoon ; the identity disc, with a little silver badge of St. Christopher attached ; a bundle of papers. Nothing. He opened a notebook—a chart of days marked-off, a list of menus, one hundred and sixty ways of filling sandwiches, countless recipes ; as usual. But at the end was a long passage of continuous writing, headed *Christmas, 1942*. It was in the form of a letter, written by Minton to his wife. 'We have a day off for Christmas, so I'll write to you, though I don't imagine I'll be able to send it to you . . .' Jervas skimmed over it, feeling embarrassed, for it was a passionately private letter. He came to a second, headed *Christmas, 1943 :* more restrained, talking largely of food, of moves from camp to camp, of hope, and then, again, the searing gush of hopeless, lost love. Jervas skipped, and with a shock came on the third heading : *Christmas, 1944*. For a moment, it was as though he saw a ghost ; the letter had been written only twenty-four hours before, on the Eve. He started to read, guiltily, almost glancing over his shoulder.

'Darling—tomorrow the third Christmas in prison and o God I pray the last without you. But we *know* now there is a second front in Europe . . . ' A wave of optimism rushed down the first page. '. . . And when it is all over, I'll be home in a couple of months and then there will be six a dozen honeymoons, o and an endless eating of food. Then, when I'm fit again, I shall go back to medicine ; that'll mean, darling, we shall starve for four years before I earn, but I can show you how to starve. It'll be heaven to starve with you . . .

'I've been ill almost since last Christmas ; they said I should have died twice—but I didn't. I *wouldn't*. It's wonderful being convalescent again, just to be alive, everything new, all the colours polished like enamel, even the grass bright and sharp as spears. This morning there were sea-gulls over the camp, though it's far from the coast—but imagine : they had seen the sea, they had wings, free to fly—and their cry, that terrible harsh unanswered call, that I heard at Bombay, at the Cape, at Gourock, on those Pembrokeshire cliffs where I said good-bye to you . . .

'Darling, only one letter from you since I said good-bye, and that I got at Bombay, written almost before I had left you. But there's mail in camp they say—perhaps I'll be lucky this time. And anyway, we shall be out so soon now, I really begin to believe again. The things we shall *make* together—all our life, our love, all our life in love, a house, a garden where our children shall run. We must have at least a dozen children, and you mustn't mind about your figure. The stouter you are, the stouter I love—o how I hate lean and hungry men ! And yet the terror here is not just hunger, nor the waste, but the sheer going-on of it all, the dying-in-life . . .'

Jervas could read no more. He closed the book. The hut was emptying about him ; everyone was going out to the Christmas service. The burial party must be almost back.

On an impulse, he rose, and went to his shelf ; thence he took the letter addressed to the dead man, the only letter unclaimed that morning. He hesitated, and then opened it.

He had read it twice before he understood it fully. It was out of context, clearly the one survivor of a series. It was not from Minton's wife, but from a cousin. 'Your son is growing fast, talking well and says Father to your photograph and lots more as well. But of course, it is lonely for the poor mite, with no father and mother, though we try to do our best . . .'

Gradually, Jervas understood that Minton's wife must have died some time ago, and that he had had a child who now lived with relations, relations who (as a vexed undercurrent of impatient resigna-tion in the letter indicated) did not relish their foster-parenthood. Minton had never known he was a widower, nor that he was a father.

For the third time that day, the same hysterical rage threatened Jervas, but collapsed. He had not the strength to sustain it again. With inane apathy he sat, looking down the empty hut. Utterly tired, he realized for the first time that condition in which so many prisoners had given up, turned their faces to the wall, and died. Life went round like an abandoned mill-wheel, grinding nothing but itself. The idea of freedom was intolerable. Why lead a blind man into the light ? He thought greyly of his wife, condemned to pilot him through the necessary years before he could go decently underground. And yet he was only forty-six. He felt a curious pang of envy for Minton, who had been so recently only twenty-five, who had had a child, who now had peace in that cold hillside.

From outside the hut, as if in mockery, the prisoners broke cheerfully, almost exultantly, into song. '*Hark, the herald angels sing* . . .'

He stared down the hut. A man had come in, and sat at a table by the door, motionless ; yet in fact, with an infinitely slow precision, he was pouring salt from a tin into an empty bottle. The stream of salt, thin as a thread, seemed to have frozen.

Jervas got up, and went to the door, and then out into the dusk, simply to move, in no direction. A little later, he came suddenly on the Christmas service, round the corner of a hut. Another carol was being announced, and he wavered on the fringe of the crowd.

'*Unto us a child is born,*' sang the prisoners, deafeningly. '*Lord of all creation* . . .' The harsh roar and swell of voices filled him, as the wind fills an empty sail. Unwillingly, he responded ; but then, as the music moved in him, inspiration struck swift as a squall. He staggered.

Of course, of course . . . —*unto us a child is born.* He and Rosemary would adopt the boy. They would have a child. Surely, the foster-parents would not object. Suddenly Major Jervas was singing with the rest of them, louder than all, as if to drive his voice westwards, breaking the fence, even to Simla.

As the service continued, the images that had haunted him that morning returned, with almost delirious intensity. Rosemary, the house in the Cotswolds, the primroses at the edge of the woods—but now a third person walked with him and Rosemary : a small boy of their own, hopping and sallying and returning.

'*Sing, choirs of angels,*' shouted Major Jervas. '*Sing in exultation* . . .'

Then the priest prayed—for peace on earth, for goodwill on earth amongst all men. The blessing followed, the congregation dispersed, noisily, and hurriedly, for beans were announced for supper.

Jervas was left alone, standing in the dark. A calm and lucid sadness of humility took possession of him. As two figures approached, he realized, with a distant surprise, that he was in prayer.

It was a sentry, preceding the Japanese Orderly Officer—a thin man with beautiful boots and hornrimmed spectacles ; he had some English. He recognized Jervas. 'I am sorry a man is dead,' he said. 'Happy Christmas. There will be three cigarettes for each man. A presento from the Emperor of Nippon.'

He and Jervas bowed stiffly at each other.

The Japanese started to move on, but stopped, playing with the hilt of his sword. 'I am sorry . . .' he said again. He sounded almost plaintive. 'But it's quite good day to die on, no, the day that Christo died ?'

THE 'FIFTIES

by OLIVE COOK *and* EDWIN SMITH

IT WOULD be difficult to imagine an array of material more conducive to speculation on the nature and achievements of mankind than a selection of the pots and pans, the pictures and poetry, the modes and manners of a certain decade in a succession of centuries. And of all the decades the 'fifties seem to have special significance. By the mid-century the character of an age has declared itself ; the promise of its early morning freshness has been fulfilled or frustrated ; and neither the influences of the preceding century nor anticipations of the one to come blur the distinctive features of the period. A Chippendale chair could not be ascribed to the end of the seventeenth or the beginning of the nineteenth centuries any more than the heavy Ionic porch, ostentatious flight of steps and plate glass of a house built in 1850 could be confused with the classical lightness of 1800.

A glance at the events and products of the 'fifties from the time when British ladies wore woad to the present heyday of the sack may arouse a similar reaction to that felt by Mr Coomaraswamy when confronted by the works of contemporary painters : 'Since the caveman, what a decline !' It may equally well evoke the spirit of optimism and fine self-confidence which prompted a well-known critic of our own 'fifties to proclaim his belief in 'a series of repeated advances.' Yet a closer view casts doubt on either standpoint. Is it possible that the Bacchanalian whirl of the Offenbach gallop is a lower form of expression than the abandon of Rock 'n' Roll ? Are the reclining figures of Henry Moore and Kenneth Armitage superior to the recumbent forms of other 'fifties, Rysbrack's nymph at Stourhead and the sleeping Jesse of Abergavenny ? Do the remarkable experiments and innovations of the 'fifties, the invention of printing with movable types in the fourteen-fifties, the replacing of oil lamps by gas, the installation of sanitary arrangements in ordinary houses, the organization of the first Cook's tour and the introduction of the sleeping-car, all achievements of the eighteen-fifties, and the explosion of the atom bomb in the nineteen-fifties, do these indicate progress or retrogradation ?

It cannot confidently be maintained that the hoop of the fifteen-fifties was inferior to that of the seventeen-fifties or to the crinoline of the eighteen-fifties. It is even doubtful whether manners have improved or declined with the passage of time. The author of *The Polite Academy*, published in 1750, asserts that a gentleman should 'pick bones clean, holding them with the finger and thumb, and leave them on the plate ; they must not be thrown down nor given to the dogs in the room.' In *Manners for Men*, written a century later, we are told : 'There is no excuse for handling bones—knives and forks suffice ; and it is only in the lowest grades of society that they are found inadequate.' If this seems to some readers suggestive of advance let them turn to rule 9 of the chapter on 'Behaviour at Meals' in *The Polite Academy* which counsels a gentleman to 'sit patiently till all the company are helped,' and compare it with the advice given in *Manners for Men* : 'It is a very old-fashioned piece of good manners to wait till everyone is served. So old-fashioned is it that it survives only among the unlettered classes. The correct thing to do nowadays is to begin eating without reference to others.'

It is not so much a development for better or worse that is suggested but a cursory survey of the 'fifties as the repetition with slight variations of the same pattern. Certain manifestations indeed seem to have no parallel. The sudden alarming upward movement of the hair style in the mid-eighteenth century, when the coiffure reached a height of as much as three feet, appears to have been an isolated phenomenon. And the no-waist fashion of our own late 'fifties, implying the abandonment of all restrictions, diverges sharply from the tight waists of the other 'fifties. But on the whole, similarities far outweigh occasional disparities.

The mid-century seems to be a period when, in the continual

struggle between northern and classical traditions from which all English art and poetry have sprung, the northern spirit triumphs. The pointed arch and stellar vaulting, both essentially anti-classical, made their appearance in the 'fifties. And it was in the mid-eighteenth century when even the chimney piece had come to resemble the façade of an antique temple that the persistent feeling for Gothic produced Strawberry Hill and embellished the Georgian façade with battlements and ogee arches. By 1850 the northern tradition had the upper hand in the Battle of the Styles. In the nineteen-fifties the pointed arch has begun to oust the flat roof of the alien continental manner in domestic architecture, and the inspiration behind the design for the new Coventry Cathedral is certainly Gothic.

It is not only in the more serious expressions of the 'fifties that basic recurrences of mood and manner can be traced. Among resemblances in fashions the dress with which Mrs Bloomer startled the world in 1850 has its counterpart in the jeans of the nineteen-fifties. And surely it is more than a coincidence that the strange preoccupation of society in the eighteen-fifties with spiritualism, hypnotism, table-turning and spirit rapping should be echoed by the concern of the mid-twentieth century with flying saucers and communications from Mars? Even the chimpanzees who recently exhibited their canvases to an admiring public are only part of the pattern of the 'fifties, for just a hundred years ago a dog belonging to Count de Rouit astonished the world by writing with a quill and employing its leisure hours in the translation of Greek into English.

THE QUEEN BIDDING ADIEU TO THE GUARDS GOING OUT TO THE CRIMEA APRIL 1854.
FROM THE BALCONY OF BUCKINGHAM PALACE.

TOYS FOR THE MILLION

NOW READY, **THE SIEGE OF SEBASTOPOL**, A GAME.

1150's

Henry II

1650's

1250's

Henry III

1550's

Oliver Cromwell

1550's

Mary I

Elizabeth I

1350's

Edward III

1450's

Henry VI

1750's

George II

1850's

Victoria

1950's

Elizabeth II

Above : 1850's

1450's : 'Cracowe' shoe

1550's

1750's

1650's

Below : Baby's lace shoes, 1850's (Louis Meier). All above from V. & A. Museum

Doll, mid-eighteenth century (V. & A. Mus.)
Below, linen stockings, mid-seventeenth
century

Perhaps the first fashion, see the lady above, is still the most effective. The 1550 Duke of Cumberland's legs (*below*) revive a pattern that surely once appeared in woad.

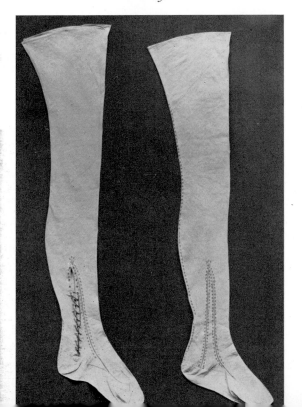

(Barry Duncan)

The precarious goddesses and gilded swags of fruit held up by ribbons, on Inigo Jones' doorcase at Wilton, are not more appropriate elements than the stag's head and other trophies of the chase adorning the Victorian door. But one superbly achieves an architectural formality, the other captures the chaos of unweeded nature.

Bristol tiles (V. & A. Mus.)
1750's

Library door, Portmeirion, Wales.   1850's

Opposite : 1650's. Wilton House, Wiltshire, the Double Cube room

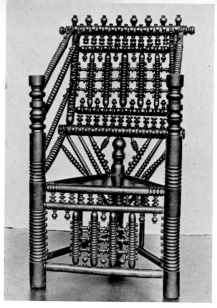

1650's

1750's

Chipped, chopped and turned, furniture had but a rustic charm until the eighteenth century, when function and fantasy mingled to perfection. The elements begin to separate by the eighteen fifties, where sometimes comfort, sometimes convenience, will oddly obtrude. The nineteen-fifty attempt at pure utility is not without fancy.

1850's

1850's

1950's

Railway bus (Barry Duncan)   *1850's*

1750's

Sedan chair

Right : the Interior of a Bus by W. M. Edgley, 1859

Below : a mobile Bubble of the nineteen-fifties

1850's

1950's

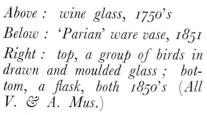

Above : wine glass, 1750's
Below : 'Parian' ware vase, 1851
Right : top, a group of birds in drawn and moulded glass ; bottom, a flask, both 1850's (All V. & A. Mus.)

Above: salt-glaze Staffordshire figure, 1750's (V. & A. Mus.)

Left: Chelsea porcelain figure of a warbler, 1755 (V. & A. Mus.)

Left, below: Staffordshire pottery figure, Comrades of the Crimea (Portmeirion)

1950's

Slipware jug by G. F. Cook

Above : 1950's. Woman *by James MacBride*

Right : 1250's Head of St. John. Wall-painting from Winchester Cathedral

Above : 1850's. Detail from Derby Day *by W. Frith (National Gall.)*

Right : 1450's. Detail from the Doom, *Wenhaston Church, Suffolk*

Opposite, 1750's. Detail from The Painter's Daughters *by Gainsborough (National Gallery)*

1050's

1750's

Above : Madonna, Inglesham Church, Wiltshire

Right : Nymph of the Grot, Stourhead, Wiltshire

Below : Sleeping Jesse, Abergavenny Church, Monmouthshire

1350's

1950's   1850's

Above : Eve and the
Serpent, by J. Burrows

Right : The Greek Slave,
by Hiram Powers.

Below : The Adoration of
the Magi, *alabaster relief
in Long Melford Church*

1450's

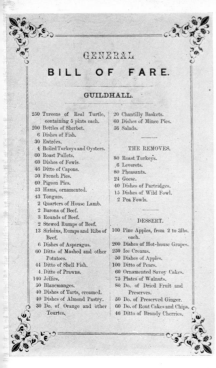

Lord Mayor's Banquet menu, 1856

Victorian dining-room scene

Opposite : the Lord Mayor's Banquet at the Guildhall, London, 1956

Seventeenth-century dining scene

Eighteenth-century book of etiquette

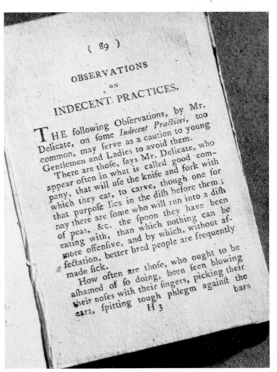

On **WEDNESDAY, JULY 1st, 1857,**

The Performance will commence with a Farce, by J. M. MORTON, Esq., entitled

A GAME OF ROMPS

Dr. Rhododendrum, (Tutor to Julian) Mr. HARLEY
Julian, (Nephew to the Marchioness) Miss DALY M. Jolivet, (a Lawyer) Mr. RAYMOND
The Marchioness, Mrs. WINSTANLEY Violet, (her Daughter) Miss KATE TERRY
Isabelle, (her Niece) Miss CARLOTTA LECLERCQ Blanche, (a Young Widow) Miss HEATH
Jeannette, (Waiting Woman to the Marchioness) Miss MURRAY

After which will be produced SHAKESPEARE's Play of

THE
TEMPEST

The shape of Britain in Ptolemy's map of 1550 (Louis Meier) and the shape of Miss Julia St. George as Ariel are perhaps but artistic conjecture, though the lady's usefulness in the energetic curtain raiser leaves, in her case, room for doubt and hope.

AN ARCHITECT'S ALPHABET

drawn and devised by MICHAEL FELMINGHAM

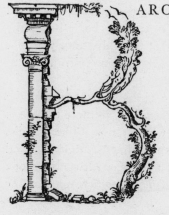

CANTHUS LEAVES abound in architecture, both Gothic and Classical, sprouting from capitals, rolling round 'freezes,' and growing in even greater profusion as interior decoration. Although there are some twenty varieties of acanthus, there are only two as far as architects are concerned : 'the one Wild, and Arm'd with Prickles ; the other ſmooth and cultivated in Gardens ; the former of which we find represented in *Gothic* buildings, and the latter in thoſe of the antique.' There is an ingenious Greek myth which accounts for the origination of the Corinthian capital. Callimachas, a clever statuary, of Athens, placed a basket of flowers upon the grave of a young Corinthian lady ; on top of the basket he placed a flat tile. On his return many days later he discovered the flower basket and tile much overgrown. It was from this that he carved the Corinthian capital. The basket he imitated in the vase or tambour ; the leaves which had grown out of it, in the scrolls or volutes, and the tile in the abacus.

AROQUE, 'properly signifying a heavy and clumsy treatment of Renaissance architecture, with coarse and florid detail; improperly used to denote a supposed "style" which has no existence as the style of any special period.' This horrifying statement can be found in the glossary of Heathcote Statham's *History of Architecture*, 1912. Must we then dismiss the splendid exuberances of Potsdam, Dresden, and Versailles as 'coarse,' and find the porcelain delicacy of Sans Souci merely 'florid' ? No, of course not. Statham was wrong, but he was not alone : the majority of his contemporaries thought as he did.

Baroque is more than a 'treatment of Renaissance architecture' ; it is the expression of an age—a time when artistic sensibilities were finely sharpened by an excess of splendours and miseries. Asymmetry ran riot among the cold rules of the Classical orders. The chiaroscuro of rough and smooth, concave and convex, the play of light on dancing cornices and fluted pilasters, brought a new sense of movement to architecture. One either likes one's friezes pulvinated, and one's pediments broken and scrolled, and one's statues fighting with flying draperies, or one does not. There can be no indifference to Baroque.

ONTEMPORARY. Only a few years ago this word was a common or garden adjective. Now we find it madly over-worked as a *Homes and Gardens* noun, glorying in a capital 'C.' Perhaps the next generation will look back on Con-temporary as we look back on Art Nouveau, thankful that it is dead. At the moment though, it is very much alive. Spurred on by architects and glossy furniture magazines, we are surrounded today by rubber plants, mobiles, Regency stripes (only on *one* wall), lemon yellow doors, and kidney-shaped chairs with gaping holes where holes should never be. 'Bring the garden into your home,' says the fashionable monthly, 'and why not take your home into the garden.' The result—a house full of plants, and a garden full of furniture.

We may take comfort, however, in the rising importance of the bathroom, and its increasing luxury and amenities. No more the arctic walls, the rusty chain, the intestine-like waste pipes. The pundits recommend murals, varied wallpapers, streamlined porcelain, and early Victorian chairs. Here one may sit at ease, with cacti on one side and a lavishly bound *D.N.B.*, or set of *The Waverley Novels* on the other.

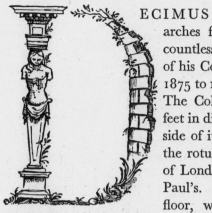

ECIMUS BURTON'S lodges and arches for Hyde Park must be known to countless Londoners; but how many know of his Colosseum, which was pulled down in 1875 to make way for Cumberland Terrace? The Colosseum consisted of a rotunda 128 feet in diameter, with a Doric portico on one side of it. The walls of the inner surface of the rotunda were painted with a panorama of London as seen from the dome of Saint Paul's. A tower stood in the centre of the floor, with balconies at different heights, and a model of the ball and cross of Saint Paul's at the top. Access to these balconies could be obtained not only by staircases but by a prototype lift, known as 'the ascending room.' This was an iron cage panelled internally and suspended from the top of the shaft; it was worked by counterweights and, presumably, some unfortunate on a winch.

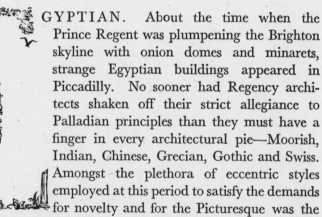

GYPTIAN. About the time when the Prince Regent was plumpening the Brighton skyline with onion domes and minarets, strange Egyptian buildings appeared in Piccadilly. No sooner had Regency architects shaken off their strict allegiance to Palladian principles than they must have a finger in every architectural pie—Moorish, Indian, Chinese, Grecian, Gothic and Swiss. Amongst the plethora of eccentric styles employed at this period to satisfy the demands for novelty and for the Picturesque was the Egyptian. Napoleon's Egyptian campaign was responsible for the French Empire's adoption of this style; and, like most French fashions, it spread here. Thomas Hope published his *Household Furniture and Interior Decoration* (1807), illustrating Egyptian rooms and details. But it quickly became apparent that the lack of principles and rules prevented its translation into actuality, and that a normal upright door was far more convenient than one which narrowed at the top.

OLLIES. If it is difficult to define exactly what constitutes a folly, the circumstances of erection will usually provide a clue. The pyramids of Egypt are just as much follies as William Beckford's cathedral home at Fonthill. Although follies were generally regarded as a prerogative of the mentally unstable, a great many sensible people erected these conceits, especially in Pope's time. The face of England developed a positive rash of delightful absurdities. The spire of a church built on a hill top to give an appearance of reality from a faraway window ; a cottage disguised as a church ; a medieval castle in decay, to point a view ; a Brobdingnagian toy fort (as at Bristol), or a strange tower for no apparent reason at all. One that appeals to me is the Needle's Eye, at Wentworth Woodhouse. It is built in the shape of a slender stone pyramid, topped with a most beautiful urn : cutting through the base is a Gothick arch resembling the top of a needle's eye. The story goes that during an evening's roistering, a gentleman wagered he could drive a coach and horses through a needle's eye. It must have been a small coach, and very accurately driven.

OTHICK with a k is usually understood as meaning that first period of the Gothic Revival in this country, for which Horace Walpole's Strawberry Hill provided a pattern. The flimsy filigree of this form of Gothic is nearer to Rococo and Chinoiserie than to medieval Gothic. In many examples of eighteenth-century Gothick it is only the repetition of the pointed arch and a plentiful crop of crockets on pinnacles which afford a link with medieval Gothic. Nowhere is this better illustrated than at Strawberry Hill. The insulation of Strawberry Hill from its counterparts may in part be due to the conflicting aims of its builders. Walpole, the true Augustan and enemy of the Gothic poets, was drawn to this style by a rather dilettante interest in Gothic archaeology. His collaborator and principal designer, Richard Bentley, however, adapted Gothic forms to his essentially Rococo imagination, and it is through him that Strawberry achieved its literary atmosphere. There were, then, two streams of thought in Gothic, the one antiquarian and the other literary. The antiquarian interest proved the stronger. The Houses of Parliament and many lesser works are the Victorian culmination of this. But, for Gochic*k*, we must confine ourselves to the latter half of the eighteenth century and the Regency, to Strawberry Hill and Arbury Hall.

OLFORD PLAN. This is the name given to Sir William Holford's design for the precincts of St Paul's Cathedral. It has inevitably aroused controversy, and the abandoning of several experimental designs. The strongest school of criticism desires a formal layout, the enclosure (and therefore isolation) of St Paul's within crescents and other balanced masses. Sir William has carefully avoided this ; he maintains that St Paul's, instead of being enclosed and therefore dominated, should be the focal point of many 'moving view points,' and should dominate its surroundings by its constant reappearance at subtly devised angles. The greatest difficulty is the reconciliation of the cathedral's scale with the growing needs of commercial offices. Canaletto has shown us how St Paul's towered over the tiny red-roofed houses of eighteenth-century London, and we have only to compare his picture with the present scene to see how completely the original scale has been lost. The present plan, whilst admitting this, does attempt a remedy in the form of open spaces—lawns and pedestrian courts, arranged to provide interesting perspectives. The most imaginative proposal, with the widest appeal, is surely the rescue of Temple Bar from exile and its re-erection between the north-west tower and the Chapter house. Personally I think the most attractive scheme was that devised by William Marlow, a disciple of Richard Wilson, in his *Capriccio* painting. This shows St Paul's rising above a Ludgate Hill transformed into a Venetian canal, swarming with gondolas instead of taxis.

CE-HOUSES. So quickly are the remains of these once common buildings disappearing, and so scanty is their literary evidence, that our descendants will probably take 'ice-houses' to mean a crossword puzzle clue for 'igloo.' Fifty years ago they were as common to any large house as stables. They were never actually 'houses,' but at best a stone cellar, or small underground chamber. Usually the building was entered at ground level, with a short flight of steps descending to the 'house.' Inside, packed with straw, was stored the ice, below which was an outlet or sump to drain away any water which formed. Frequently fruit was stored on top of the ice. Although ice-houses were not known in this country until the seventeenth century, they were used by many of the ancient civilizations. Once introduced here, they soon became indispensable, owing to the difficulty of preserving food in pre-refrigeration days. There may well be some truth in the assumption that the prodigious eighteenth-century appetite for spices was occasioned by the need to disguise rotten food. The only fault with the ice-house was its reliance on hard frosts to provide thick ice on a nearby river, or lake : thin ice would melt before it reached the ice-house. Many countrymen must still remember, as boys, cutting ice from the river bank, and returning with the laden carts and steaming horses to a quaint little door in the snow.

AMES GIBBS (1682–1754) is generally considered to have been the greatest of those architects who succeeded Wren. There has to be some justification for such a statement when we consider that his contemporaries were Thomas Archer, Colin Campbell, Henry Flitcroft, William Kent, Sir John Vanbrugh, John James, Thomas Ripley, and Nicholas Hawkesmoor. A formidable array indeed, and representative of many different variations upon the Georgian theme. Vanbrugh, like Wren, derived his inspiration from France, but Gibbs and the great majority of his contemporaries turned to the Italy of Bernini, Borromini, and Palladio. It was not so much a question of their doubting the mathematical genius of Wren, but rather a sudden revaluation of Inigo Jones. Hawkesmoor endeavoured to combine classic with Gothic, as in Christ Church, Spitalfields ; Archer achieved a certain success in adopting the Italian Baroque, helped by Lord Burlington ; Colin Campbell transplanted Italian villas to Mereworth and Chiswick ; and William Kent tried his hand at practically everything. In effect each group of architects had its own idea about interpreting the Italian influence in England. Baroque was discarded almost as soon as it reached us ; Hawkesmoor's Gothic was too early and too late ; Palladianism did better in later days. So it was that Gibbs typified his time. In this he was fortunate, but undoubtedly it was to the imaginative monumental quality of his works that he owed his success. The Senate House at Cambridge, the Radcliffe Camera, Oxford, and St Martin-in-the-Fields show this quality to superb effect.

 EEPS went out with the coming of gunpowder—at which date 'The Englishman's Home' legend suffered its first setback—but until that time they remained largely unassailable. Our countryside is still rich in the lichen-tinted remains of these once exceptionally functional relics. Standing within their encircling curtain walls, which are now most often merely the briefest indication of tumbled masonry, their hollow eyes stare fixedly over landscapes greatly changed. Where once deep forests rolled away to the horizon, suburbia sprawls. The keep was the crow's nest, from which ample warning could be given of an advancing foe. By the time these unfortunates arrived, the garrison would have packed all valuables inside the keep and be waiting on the roof, quietly boiling water and lead, and amassing heavy objects with which to welcome their visitors. Often brattices (timber galleries) were projected over the walls so that fire could be directed on to the base of the wall. Also projecting towers were built to cover the walls with flanking fire, as at Conisborough. Early keeps are usually square ; it was not until the early fourteenth century that round keeps were built. The destruction of keeps by prising away the corner stones made this inevitable.

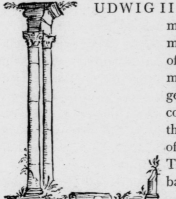

L UDWIG II of Bavaria, or 'Mad Ludwig,' as he is more popularly known, was the last monarch to attempt to rival the grandeurs of Versailles and Potsdam. Weak in matters of state, he was fanatically energetic where his building projects were concerned : a fanaticism perhaps akin to the music of Wagner, which provided one of his chief sources of inspiration. Throughout all the styles he indulged in— baroque, medieval, moorish and oriental —the stamp of his personality is clearly defined. It is no wonder that a mind so overloaded with visions of such ponderous complexity should eventually become deranged. One of the most successful of his castles is the Baroque palace of Linderhof (1870). Set in dramatic mountain scenery and surrounded by baroque gardens, it owes its success to the harmonious relation of garden to exterior, and exterior to interior. Inside it is a riot of rococo, each room a glittering cabinet of swirling ornament. His greatest glory is undoubtedly Herrenchiemsee, in which he embodied his fervent admiration for the absolutism of 'Le Roi Soleil.' Following the pattern of Versailles and including a Hall of Mirrors, and a Royal Bedchamber only slightly different from those at Versailles, this palace contains the last fine flourishings of German Rococo art.

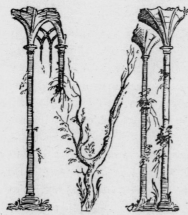

M URAL PAINTING. It is surely not strange to think of mural painting as a part of architecture (and to consider it with columns, walls, and windows), for it has always been so regarded in the past. We cannot delve far into the history of any period of architecture without discovering its employment of murals. Greek, Roman, Renaissance, Palladian, Baroque, Gothic—all have employed the artist's brush to enhance architectural effect. So closely are the two arts connected that it is true to say that mural painting has played the concerto accompaniment to the orchestral variations of architecture. When architecture has reached its highest points of development, so has the mural. We have but to think of the Renaissance, with Leonardo da Vinci, Michaelangelo and Masaccio, and the Baroque with Tiepolo and his contemporaries, to prove this point. Today, in what many regard as a period of architectural staleness, the mural artist has endless possibilities. For today the patronage of the aristocratic and wealthy individual has been supplanted by that of industry. Unfortunately, industry and commerce can never supply that warm and personal satisfaction that is the reward of the artist working to please the private patron. I am thinking particularly of Rex Whistler, for if murals are to be judged by the personal pleasure they give to their owners, as well as their architectural value, no other artist is his equal. How would he fare today, I wonder, when the country houses which once were flattered by his gifted work are perilously near to fossilization ?

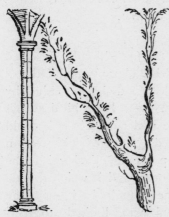EW DELHI. It is unfortunate that time and history have conspired to separate us from Sir Edwin Lutyens' greatest triumph. Those who care must feel rather as a Frenchman would now feel had Versailles been built in Tibet. 'It is expected, and assumed, that the representatives of British sovereignty beyond the seas shall move in a setting of proper magnificence ; and that in India, particularly, the temporal power shall be hedged with the divinity of earthly splendour. To satisfy this expectation, New Delhi was designed and created.' So wrote Robert Byron, in 1931. These words ring sadly and strangely in this land of the Welfare State. During the Delhi Durbar of 1911, King George V proclaimed the building of New Delhi as the capital of Imperial India. The following year, in the face of much angry criticism, Sir Edwin Lutyens was called upon to provide designs ; it was not until 1929 that the Viceroy moved into his unfinished palace. It occasionally happens (as with St Paul's Cathedral) that one man, possessing the courage born of knowing himself to be right, will triumph over the timidity of lesser men.

RGANIC ARCHITECTURE, as practised by the controversial American architect Frank Lloyd Wright, is the blending of architecture with its geographic surroundings. Those wishing to see the practical results of his theories should read the book he wrote on the subject. This illustrates a variety of milk crates, orange boxes and crashed aeroplanes demonstrating his theories. Frank Lloyd Wright is a persuasive writer and talker, but when confronted with his projected 'Mile High' sky city I fail to see how any building tottering a mile into the sky can be organically related to the surrounding earth. This mile-high needle is envisaged for Chicago, and will accommodate 130,000 of that city's population. Atomic-powered elevators link the 528 floors ; designs also include parking space for 15,000 cars and 100 helicopters. But we shall reach the moon first.

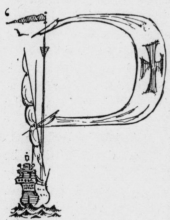

ORTABLE COTTAGE designed for the Use of Emmigrants and Others.' So runs the title of a design published by J. C. Loudon in 1833. From his drawings it is difficult to understand how it could possibly be called a 'cottage.' The wooden framework appears identical with the modern greenhouse, and it weighed little more than one hundredweight. The 'accommodation' was limited to two rooms, twelve feet square and eight feet high, with a 'stove of wrought iron, for lightness. This, then, is the ancestor of the modern caravan. For his *Ambulatory Cottage* Loudon advised only one family room, with wheels beneath the floor. 'With such a portable cottage, [together with 'Siebe's pumps' for 'water from any neighbouring well or brook,' and 'Perkin's tubes for circulating hot water under compression'], . . . a man with £200 or £300 a year might enjoy in Britain as much rural beauty and variety, as would cost another with a fixed town and country residence as many thousands.'

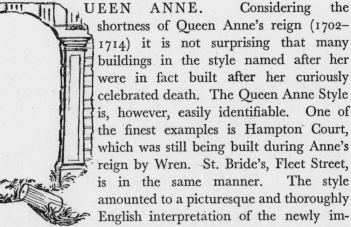

UEEN ANNE. Considering the shortness of Queen Anne's reign (1702–1714) it is not surprising that many buildings in the style named after her were in fact built after her curiously celebrated death. The Queen Anne Style is, however, easily identifiable. One of the finest examples is Hampton Court, which was still being built during Anne's reign by Wren. St. Bride's, Fleet Street, is in the same manner. The style amounted to a picturesque and thoroughly English interpretation of the newly imported Classical Style. Upon a box of red bricks the architect applied heavily quoined sash windows with a central Classical or semi-Baroque doorway. Carved stone ornament in the form of flaming urns, wreaths, ribbons, flowers and crossed palms, enlivened the warm brickwork ; great use was also made of chimneys, dormer windows and gables. It was in fact the sweet infancy of Georgian architecture.

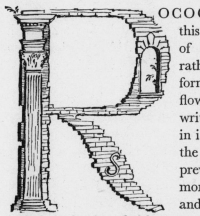

OCOCO. Sir Osbert Sitwell has called this 'the supreme dialect of the language of Baroque.' What is Rococo ? Or rather what *was* it ? It was primarily a form of decoration composed of shells, flowers, leaves, branches, vines, and rocks, writhing in sinuous curves. Its value lay in its adaptability to architecture and all the decorative arts, lending them a previously unknown freedom and harmony. This resulted in a unity of interior and exterior, room and furniture, table and chair, book and title-page. We are told that rococo derives from the French word *rocailles*, after the rock grottoes of Louis XIV's Versailles. This is no doubt true. It does lead, though, to the dangerous assumption that rococo was an entirely French invention. I feel that it is an art more deeply rooted in German soil. In their love of the grotesque and delicate fantasy, Hieronymous Bosch and Dürer must be the true ancestors of rococo ; not graphically but intellectually.

UBTERRANEAN ARCHITECTURE. In direct contrast to the aerial visionaries, such as William Beckford and Gustave Eiffel, there are those who realize their architectural ambitions underground. The fifth Duke of Portland is the prime example. Derision is inevitably the inheritance of the unconventional, but as long as we realize the value of eccentricity in an increasingly humdrum world he will not be altogether forgotten. During the eighteen-seventies he employed some fifteen thousand men at Welbeck Abbey, both above and below ground. A ballroom of vast proportions, libraries, conservatories, kitchens and pantries, and many lesser offices were the subterranean fruits of their labours. It is pleasant to know that on commencing work each workman was presented with a donkey and an umbrella. Why, I cannot discover.

Perhaps his most ambitious venture was the underground tunnel over a mile long. Wide enough to take two carriages, and lit by gas lamps, it dipped under the lake and across the park to Worksop. At the station his Grace was lifted in his carriage like a cage bird and deposited on a special flat truck, and so conveyed to London. With drawn blinds he was able to travel from Welbeck Abbey to his London club without being seen. Mad? Perhaps, but then what is sanity?

EMPLE BAR, once the site of Sir Christopher Wren's splendid arch, is now marked by a monument erected in 1880, a monument which is hardly a worthy successor to one of the Strand's finest architectural features, and little less of an obstruction. The first known boundary at this point was an iron chain stretched across the road. For anything that happened west of this the City Fathers would take no responsibility. This was in the early fourteenth century. By 1533 it had become necessary to build a more permanent structure. Accordingly a wooden gate and guard house were erected. In all the journeys of kings and queens to the City of London this is where they were and still are received. It was here, for instance, that Charles II knocked, on his jubilant restoration. Six years later Old Temple Bar was pulled down. Wren was commissioned to design a new one, as dignified and imposing an arch as possible. In 1672 the new arch was opened with much pomp. Together with Wren's statues the arch was further decorated by the placing of traitors' heads on spikes. In 1684 the 'Rye House Plot brought the first trophy to the Golgotha at Wren's Temple Bar'; this consisted of the forequarter of Sir Thomas Armstrong, the head having been placed over Westminster Hall. Horace Walpole tells us that at one time it was possible to hire a spy-glass for a half-penny to see such gory attractions the better. In 1772 the last head was blown down. Nearly a century later Wren's Temple Bar itself was gone, with no trace but a Victorian Monument and a café which bears its name.

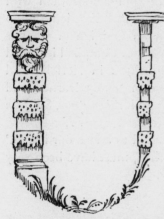

RNS. Apart from the modern copies, which are most often distortions, urns are the prerogative of the Age of Reason. A visitor to most fashionable eighteenth-century houses will find them, balancing on pedestals, hiding in niches, sunning themselves on Augustan roofs, reflected in water, and appearing whitely in unfrequented glades. As architectural taste paled, thinned into Adamesque filigree, and finally died, so did hydriolatry. But, to turn to the heyday of its popularity; 'tis ye nicest Thing in ye world to place an Urn judiciously, so yt it may have as solemn an Effect as possible; be seen at a proper distance; & have just Scenery enough around it to make ye whole picturesque,' writes William Shenstone to Lady Luxborough in 1749. Their letters are full of the most detailed reasoning on urns : and their decoration. 'I have some little Fondness for ye surrounding wreath with 4 Knotts— as I think the Urn should have *some* decoration where ye Pedestal has any.' Nothing is more typical of the age than Shenstone's closing lines : 'Let Mr Williams finish his Piece ; give his Urn a little-bolder Relievo ; try ye Effect of a Lyre & Festoons ; bring a little Water before ye Urn from left to Right, which then may turn & lose itself amongst ye Trees . . . —I fancy this would render it no unamiable Picture.'

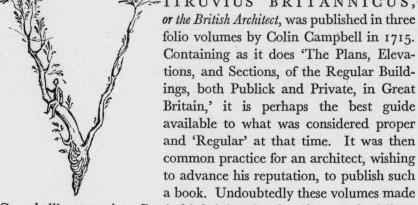

ITRUVIUS BRITANNICUS, *or the British Architect*, was published in three folio volumes by Colin Campbell in 1715. Containing as it does 'The Plans, Elevations, and Sections, of the Regular Buildings, both Publick and Private, in Great Britain,' it is perhaps the best guide available to what was considered proper and 'Regular' at that time. It was then common practice for an architect, wishing to advance his reputation, to publish such a book. Undoubtedly these volumes made Campbell's reputation. But in his brief preface he advances the following plausible reason ; 'The General Esteem that Travellers have for Things that are foreign is in nothing more conſpicuous than with regard to Building . . . It's owing to this Miſtake in Education, that ſo many of the *British* Quality have ſo mean an Opinion of what is performed in our own Country.' In these volumes Campbell included a number of his own designs, notably Houghton in Norfolk, and Stourhead in Wiltshire, together with those of 'many learned and ingenious Gentlemen, as Sir *Christopher Wren*, Sir *William Bruce*, Sir *John Vanbrugh*, Mr *Archer*, Mr *Wren*, Mr *Wynne*, Mr *Talman*, Mr *Hawkeſmore*, Mr *James*, &c., who have all greatly contributed to adorn our iſland.' To have one's house illustrated in *Vitruvius* then, must have been very comparable to having it in *Country Life* today.

INDOWS. Aesthetically, I suppose, the most perfect window forms are the Gothic pointed arch and rose windows—the glories of Gothic architecture. The pointed arch window derived originally from the grouping together of several lancet windows under one large arch. The tympanum or blank space between the soffit of the large arch and the heads of the smaller ones was filled with circles, or quatrefoils ; gradually the irregular stone masses thus left came to be pierced with tracery. It was, perhaps, a window of this style in Stansted Chapel that inspired Keats to write :

> A casement high and triple-arch'd there was,
> All garlanded with carven imag'ries
> Of fruits, and flowers, and bunches of knot-grass,
> And diamonded with panes of quaint device,
> Innumerable of stains and splendid dyes,
> As are the tiger-moth's deep-damask'd wings ;
> And in the midst, 'mong thousand heraldries,
> And twilight saints, and dim emblazonings,
> A shielded scutcheon blush'd with blood of queens and kings.

Such a window is more of a tapestry of light upon the walls and has little to do with functional lighting. It is curious to reflect that whilst hotly debating this problem of lighting the Victorians everywhere employed the Gothic window, even in the most secular places. Many involved theories have been advanced to determine the size of window necessary for a given room size. Few could be simpler than that devised by the eighteenth-century architect Sir William Chambers. He writes : 'I have generally added the depth and height [I presume, width] of the rooms on the principal floor together, and taken one eighth part thereof for the width of the window.' I wonder what we do today ?

 IS as much an unknown quantity to myself as it is to mathematicians. I cannot recall anything architectural beginning with 'X,' and no amount of ransacking and pillaging of architectural dictionaries has revealed anything remotely intelligible to me, or likely to be of interest to anyone else. It seemed a pity not to complete my alphabet, and also to waste the wonderful words I have discovered ; so, for those who find amusement in pitting their knowledge against the obscure—in short, for fellow Serendips—here are my gleanings : Xaintes ; Xamete ; Xat ; Xenaios ; Xenodocheum ; Xyst.

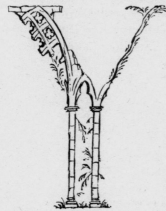

EVELE. Henry Yevele (*c.* 1370–1400) is one of the few English medieval architects to be remembered today. It has been said that he gave to English architecture the same qualities of unity and strength which Chaucer gave to our literature. It amounted in both cases to a fresh appreciation of the English tradition, which had so long been subject to continental influence. It cannot be claimed for Yevele that he invented the Perpendicular style, but his imaginative use of it did much to enrich its development. The nave and west cloister of Westminster Abbey, Westminster Hall, the nave of Canterbury Cathedral, London Charterhouse, and the Abbot's House, Westminster, are his larger works which remain least altered by time.

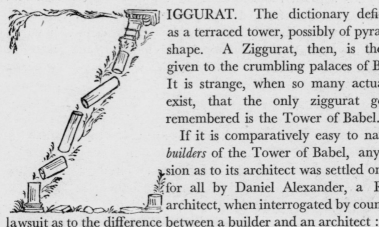

IGGURAT. The dictionary defines this as a terraced tower, possibly of pyramidical shape. A Ziggurat, then, is the name given to the crumbling palaces of Babylon. It is strange, when so many actual ruins exist, that the only ziggurat generally remembered is the Tower of Babel.

If it is comparatively easy to name the *builders* of the Tower of Babel, any discussion as to its architect was settled once and for all by Daniel Alexander, a Regency architect, when interrogated by counsel in a lawsuit as to the difference between a builder and an architect :

'An architect, sir, conceives the design, prepares the plan, draws out the specification—in short, supplies the mind. The builder is merely the machine ; the architect the power that puts the machine together and sets it going.'

'Oh, very well, Mr Architect, that will do. A very ingenious distinction without a difference. Do you happen to know who was the architect of the Tower of Babel ?'

'There was no architect, sir. Hence the confusion.'

THE FACE
IN THE WINDOW

Text by NORMAN SCARFE
Photographs by BIRKIN HAWARD

TO ENJOY the fragmentary survivals of medieval stained glass one must visit many churches, which is to become an antiquary, a bishop, an archdeacon, or at least a rural dean. The likelihood is that one becomes an antiquary, but antiquaries are well known to be interested in scratch-dials, or squints, or wodewoses, or blocked-up low-side windows, to the exclusion of all else. If we are not to be of that number, if we actually hope to see something of how other people lived in the Middle Ages, will their glass pictures convey to us any more than that they were rather idolatrous Christians, interested purely in Biblical images, the mystique of an unreal world ? Can we look up into the traceried window of a York church and respond instinctively as we do at Althorp in the almost embarrassing presence of the Duc de Chevreuse, by the younger Pourbus, one of the most vivid of Renaissance portraits in oil ? Of course we cannot. But if we look patiently we shall see a great deal more than the beautiful expressions of piety that we may have been led to expect.

We must accept the fact that piety was the main motive and inspiration in the ecclesiastical art of the Middle Ages. But that other elements were present was already clear to the nonconformist mind of Sir John Oldcastle, the Lollard, at the time of his trial in 1413, when he professed : 'As to images he understood that these were not of faith but ordained by the Church to be calendars to lay and ignorant folk to bring to mind the Passion of Christ and the martyrdom and good living of other saints, but if a man did the worship to dead images that is due to God or put such hope and trust in them as he should do towards God, he did in that the great sin of maumetry or idolatry.'

Oldcastle was removed, but imperceptibly the Church *was* losing its hold over human individuals. As human beings the donors of windows had long been themselves appearing in the glass pictures amid the martyrdoms and lives of the saints. It was a natural development and not difficult to justify ; but it was the kind of tendency that led to the disruption of the Church in the century after Oldcastle's.

[53]

The magnificent series of windows round the choir of Tewkesbury Abbey provides a good example from as early as the early 1340's. A Doom, or Last Judgment, the medieval conception of the end of their order, occupies the central window, while the windows on either side portray the prophets, patriarchs, and kings from the ancient world of the Bible. On either side of them, from the relatively modern world, stand the heads of the great family that had virtually founded the abbey's fortune in 1087 (see detail of Robert Fitz-Hamon, illustration A), and remained closely connected with it down to the erection of these windows. All the military figures, whether representing historic personages like Fitz-Hamon, a friend and henchman of both Rufus and Henry I, who endowed the abbey out of the proceeds of the conquest of Glamorgan, or contemporary persons from the world of Edward II and Edward III, are identifiable equally by heraldry alone. That their faces are so similar is due not to any supposed family likeness, but to the fact that a mere shorthand symbol for a face was employed. Indeed, the unpractised, unconvinced drawing of Fitz-Hamon's nose may be instructively compared with that of the archangel Michael's in illustration R. If anything, Michael's is the more credible. But at Tewkesbury there is one exception to this rule. In the central window a female figure kneels naked at her Judgment. She is presumably the posthumous donor of the whole scheme of windows, Eleanor de Clare, widow of two of the men represented. Her face is more carefully drawn, and there is a certain realism about her navel and her collar-bones.

If hers is the one truly fourteenth-century personality in the Tewkesbury glass, we can nevertheless learn more about the society she knew from figures like Fitz-Hamon's. Apart from his ludicrous face, like that of some Bulgar expecting the perpetration of the Atrocities, he looks very much as Edward's professional officers must have looked during the pantomime campaign of 1339 and the more serious business of Sluys and Tournai in 1340, as the Hundred Years War began. He is armed with a lance (it extends below the photograph) and a sword and is shown in the compromise between mail and plate armour that gave way completely to plate in the course of the war. The green ailettes on the shoulders are not unlike those worn by Sir Geoffrey Luttrell (of the Luttrell Psalter) in the famous and exactly contemporary picture that shows him mounted and receiving his helmet, his shield and his lance from his lady.

At the other end of the Hundred Years War, Anne Harling, a Norfolk heiress, married a distinguished Suffolk soldier, Sir William Chamberlain, K.G., and, after his death in 1462, married another Suffolk knight, Sir Robert Wingfield (detail in illustration B). He is depicted (along with the Adoration Scene, K, and much else), in the east window of the noble parish church of East Harling, at prayer, presumably as one of the donors. The date is perhaps the time of his death, in 1480, and unlike the knights of 1340, he is not only identified heraldically, by the pairs of wings (punning on his name) on his surcoat, but by being carefully drawn in what must surely have been a likeness. He was Controller of Edward IV's household, and wears the Yorkist collar of gold suns and white roses.

Whether or not it is a faithful portrait, it seems admirably expressive of devotion, well calculated to serve as example to 'lay and ignorant folk.' But Sir John Oldcastle and his like professed to fear that the images themselves would attract the worship due to God. The remainder of the great east window at East Harling is largely devoted to a series of pictures of the Joys and Sorrows of the Blessed Virgin Mary. Illustration K is a very close reproduction of one of the Joys, the Adoration of the Shepherds. If Sir Robert Wingfield's picture is a true portrait, these pictures are painted with full contemporary realism, by an artist or artists of the 'Norwich School,' and are obviously based on contemporary faces. Those who believe too implicitly in 'the Waning of the Middle Ages,' in the exclusively morbid pre-occupations of fifteenth-century artists, might pay more heed to the writing in the windows. This picture also reminds us that East Harling stands in age-long sheep country, and Norwich likewise. There is an ancient tradition, echoed in lines of a Coventry Corpus Christi play, that the shepherds were listening to pipes when the angel appeared. The painting certainly suggests that Norfolk shepherds, like their brethren the world over, piped to pass the time. It gives us a particular idea of a Norfolk twin-belled pipe, and also of a Norfolk sheepskin cap.

This is part of a typical but unusually complete series of instructional windows. The other subjects, each with its incidental set of reflections of fifteenth-century provincial life, are the Annunciation, the Visitation of St Elizabeth, the Nativity, the Adoration of the Kings, the Presentation in the Temple, Christ among the Doctors, the Marriage Feast at Cana, the Betrayal, the Crucifixion, the Deposition, the Resurrection, the Ascension, Pentecost, and the Assumption of the

Blessed Virgin. (For more detail, see Christopher Woodforde's fine book : *The Norwich School of Glass-painting in the Fifteenth Century*, 1950.) Complete though this sounds, it occupies only one window, and the remaining windows of the church have lost their ancient glass, with the exception of some of the topmost tracery lights, which contain pictures of angels.

Angels in stained glass survive in relatively large numbers because their natural habitat was the roof and upper windows, out of the reach of the Reformers and of William Dowsing, the official East Anglian iconoclast of the seventeenth-century Puritans. Fifteenth-century people were given a sense of the lively presence of angels, and the curly-headed one in St Peter Hungate, Norwich (illustration C), delightfully drawn, shows what wonders they must have contributed to the adventure of going to church. Another angelic head, wearing a diadem, is preserved in a blissful fragment at Bawburgh (N). At Bale (also in Norfolk), a second contemporary musical instrument is played by an angel (D) : a cittern, which he strums with a plectrum. (A contemporary instrument in both senses, for the zither is a modern Tyrolese form of cittern.) Illustration R is a detail of the arresting picture at Martham, in Broadland, of the archangel Michael holding the scales in which souls are being weighed. The placid inscrutability of his face distracts attention from the fact that he is carefully tipping the balance in favour of the good. (The top fragment of forehead and nimbus is a modern restoration.)

So far we have looked only at glass of the fourteenth and fifteenth centuries. Yet the twelfth and thirteenth centuries are, with reason, regarded as the great period of glass-painting. In those years, as Sir Herbert Read has concisely explained, 'a technique of geometric design was evolved which by virtue of its simplicity, its forceful stylization, and the sobriety of its colour performed fitly the dual function of all medieval art, teaching in easily legible pictures the history of the church and its dogmas, and as a perfectly adapted member giving radiance and colour to that most rich and final unity in the history of art—a Gothic cathedral.' For the most part 'forceful stylization' is undoubtedly the key to the glass designs of these earlier centuries. The object is sacred indoctrination—not profane reflection. The four holy figures (illustration F) from Le Mans Cathedral are both impersonal and impassive, and all they tell us of their age and society is that in ecclesiastical art all detail was truly subordinate to the

Opposite : Plate A
Robert Fitz-Hamon
Tewkesbury Abbey

B

Above: Detail of the kneeling figure of Sir Robert Wingfield, *c.* 1480, East Harling, Norfolk. Is it a portrait? Almost certainly. Carefully drawn lips and eyebrows distinguish the 'life school' of the fifteenth-century Norwich artists. The colouring, gold, silver and black, was suggested by the Yorkist collar: gold suns and white roses. *Below:* Heavenly angel, St Peter Hungate, Norwich. Her message—part of the *Nunc Dimittis*

C

D

E

Above: both are from Bale, Norfolk; the colouring mainly gold and white, the delineation of the features most engaging. D is now known locally as 'Tommy Steele'. E portrays the Virgin Mary at her Annunciation.

Below: Le Mans Cathedral. Notice the expressive use of the elongated curved hands

F

G

These and the top picture opposite are from the Miracles of St
Thomas, 1220–1225, in Canterbury Cathedral. These photographs are
of detail and do not show the artificial shape of the armatures (iron-

H

J

frames) within which the artist worked: it would not be guessed from the extraordinarily expressive freedom of movement of the figures. *Below*: Adoration of the Shepherds, East Harling, Norfolk

K

L

M

N

P

The pictures opposite are from Canterbury, except the contrasting angel from Baw-burgh, Norfolk. Above is the Prophet Zephaniah, designed by an Oxford glass painter, Master Thomas, *c.* 1400, for Winchester College, and now in the Victoria and Albert Museum, London. It may be a prototype of much of the York glass. Zephaniah wrote one of the more alarming little books in the Bible. The son of Cushi, he begins his prophecy: 'I will utterly consume all things from off the land, saith the Lord.' No wonder those eyes are so wide open! He goes on: 'This is the rejoicing city that dwelt carelessly, that said in her heart, I am, and there is none beside me: how is she become a desolation, a place for beasts to lie down in: everyone that passeth by her shall hiss, and wag his hand.'

design and to the doctrinal function. Yet the artists in the thirteenth century and even in the twelfth did in fact occasionally draw from life. The occasions were whenever the stock, conventional figures failed them.

For instance, possibly as early as the second quarter of the twelfth century, the hanging of some thieves was depicted in the Pierpont Morgan 'Life of St Edmund,' and is not alone in showing remarkable signs of naturalism. A century later, at Canterbury, the miraculous attributes of the lately re-enshrined martyr, Archbishop Thomas Becket, provided the subject of an array of astonishing pictures, not of remote, scriptural or historic scenes, but of nearly Chaucerian episodes in contemporary life. (They may be studied more fully in Bernard Rackham's magnificent book : *The Ancient Glass of Canterbury Cathedral*, 1949.) At this time a mastery of dramatic line had been achieved, and it coincided with a brilliant perfection of glass manufacture : see illustrations G, H, J, L, M and P for details. The one roughly contemporary literary work of comparable human interest in England is Jocelin of Brakelond's *Chronicle*.

Illustration G reveals the terror of the plague in the household of Sir Jordan Fitz-Eisulf of Pontefract, who had known Becket in his lifetime, but who neglected to fulfil his vow to visit the shrine and give thanks to the martyr for the restoration to life of his ten-year-old son. (Illustration M shows a detail of two attendants at the foot of the sick boy's bed.) Thereupon a blind, lame leper named Gimp (an appropriate character, well-named, one might think, in a story of this kind and date) was thrice visited by the martyr and told to warn Jordan what would happen if he failed to fulfil his vow. Jordan ignored the warning, and an elder son died. In illustration G, three sons (I imagine) press hands to head in anguish while (in the rest of the picture) their father and mother are too ill to rise from their chairs by the deathbed : St Thomas with sword drawn appears over the corpse, and an inscription (translated) reads : 'The piling up of vengeance, a sick house, and offspring dead.' Jordan and wife quickly made for Canterbury, and emptied a bowl of gold and silver on the shrine.

Sickness, and its miraculous cure, is also the subject of illustration J, a detail in which a lady, possibly 'Juliana de Puintel,' swooning against a high-backed chair, suffers from vomiting, 'is tormented in her bowels.' She is cured by St Thomas. Illustration H illustrates the treatment of the demented : probably a woman called 'Matilda of

[65]

Cologne.' Two men belabour her with birches as she approaches the shrine. In illustration P, the lunatic brought by flailing keepers is a local man, Henry of Fordwich, and 'dangerous.' However

Amens accedit.
Orat sanusque recedit.

One hears some young monk proud of his learning, pronouncing this tag for the benefit of less lettered, but nonetheless hopeful, pilgrims. Henry's notable profile has a look of Peter Grimes, if not of Peter Quint, in a more modern dramatic episode.

The faintly Rembrandtesque group of Orientals in illustration L is inscribed : 'These are the Pharisees, contemptuous of the Word of God.' An accompanying medallion shows a miraculous draught of fishes with the inscription : 'The word is the net. The boat of Peter is this house of piety. The Jewish fish who make holes in the net are the Pharisees.' Nothing could be at once more symbolic and explicit. Another episode in this series at Canterbury concerns a Bedfordshire man who was sentenced and awarded an unjust penalty : it registers a vivid protest against the savagery of contemporary punishment. Lessons might be learnt by pilgrims of all ages from all parts. Bobby of Rochester is a boy who was drowned in the Medway while out stoning frogs. William, a carpenter of Kellet (Lancs), splits his own shin with an axe ; Adam the forester is shot with an arrow through the throat by a poacher ; a groom of Roxburgh is rescued from drowning in the Tweed ; an infant son of the Earl of Clare is cured of hernia ; and, finally, William, an engineer of Gloucester, employed by the Archbishop of York (an opponent of Becket), is buried by a fall of earth while laying water-pipes on the archbishop's estate at Church-down. St Thomas's net was doubtless holed by Pharisees, too, but nobody can say that it was not cast wide. Its spread enclosed the lives of people in every corner of the kingdom, and they are reflected in these great, glittering cathedral windows : motionless for a century and a half before their descendants were reflected in the mind of Chaucer, they retain the power to move.

The Editor and the photographer express their thanks to the ecclesiastical authorities and incumbents for the facilities given for photographing windows in the cathedrals and parish churches mentioned.

THE GOOLE CAPTAIN

by LEONARD CLARK

ONE day as I walked by Crocodile Mansions
I met a young woman, sea-green were her eyes,
And she was loud weeping by the banks of the Humber,
O, bitter the sound of her sobs and her sighs.

I asked this young woman why she was sore weeping,
'Pray, tell me,' I said, 'why you grieve by the tide ?'
And when I had put my arm tightly around her,
In a voice like a sea bird she sadly replied,

'I was born, sir, at Wetwang, but I left the East Riding,
With the cows and the sheep as a girl I would roam,
And if I were back with my father and brothers
I'd ne'er leave again the sweet fields of my home.'

So I led her so gently past Crocodile Mansions,
And I took her so gently by the banks of the Humber,
She gave herself freely, her eyes and her kisses,
And I gave her a gold ring and a necklet of amber.

When we parted at stardown no more was she weeping,
But the very next morning as I sailed out with the tide,
She waved to me gaily as we hove round the headland
And I yearned for her beauty to be by my side.

O, I sailed for a year and a day to the Indies
And came back to England one green day in spring
But I had forgotten the girl with the green eyes,
The necklet of amber, the little gold ring.

But as I was strolling down the Land of Green Ginger
While our ship loaded up with a cargo for Poole,
The people they looked at me strangely and whispered,
'O, beware of the faithless young captain from Goole.'

So I went off at once to Crocodile Mansions
To look for my dear love with sea-green eyes,
But no-one would tell me nor answer my questions,
O, bitter my heart then and empty my sighs.

Then I met in 'The Dragon' a drunken old sailor
Who told me he'd seen her with a necklet of amber,
A little gold ring and her eyes green and staring
Floating far out to sea by the banks of the Humber.

And I walked for the last time by Crocodile Mansions,
My heart was so full I shed never a tear
O, I looked at the sea and I looked at the Humber
And in every green wave were the eyes of my dear.

'LOWESTOFT'

A Bicentenary Appreciation by NOEL TURNER

LITTLE PIGS and cowrie shells may seem remote from the ceramic products of an East Anglian fishing port : but there is a connection, for the word 'porcelain' comes from the Italian *porcellana*, derived rather delightfully from *porcella*, a cowrie shell or literally a piglet.

The collecting of porcelain was high fashion in England in the eighteenth century. For some time past Chinese porcelain had been brought home by merchantmen and had provided a colourful link with the mysterious and alluring Orient. In some of the great houses porcelain rooms had been designed to hold and display these fragile treasures. Then, in the first decade of the century, the secret of porcelain making was discovered at Meissen near Dresden in Saxony —a secret which spread over the mainland of Europe during the next thirty years, and in the early 1740's was independently rediscovered in England. Within the next ten years porcelain factories were established at Chelsea and Bow in London, at Longton Hall in Staffordshire, at Derby and at Worcester.

The fame of these factories reached the far corners of the country, even to remote and rural Suffolk where in April, 1756, an advertisement in the *Ipswich Journal* announced that the Worcester factory had opened a London warehouse at Aldersgate. It is not, therefore, surprising that when Hewlin Luson, squire of Gunton, near Lowestoft, discovered a fine clay on his estate later in the same year he sent it to London to be tested as china clay. Having been assured of its suitability he set up a kiln and tried unsuccessfully to establish a porcelain manufactory.

· At this time Lowestoft, standing on the Suffolk coast at England's most easterly point, was a small but flourishing fishing port, and it is to its credit that four local men were sufficiently resourceful, despite the initial failure, to exploit Squire Luson's discovery. In 1757 Robert Browne, a chemist, joined with Obed Aldred and John Richman, both fishing boat owners, and Philip Walker to found the Lowestoft China Factory.

The porcelain made at Lowestoft was soft-paste or 'artificial,' as was that from most of the eighteenth-century English factories, and was produced by mixing fusible glass or frit with china clay. At Lowestoft, as at Chelsea, Bow and Derby, bone-ash was introduced to improve the fire-resistant quality of the china. Hard-paste or 'true' porcelain, as made in China, consisted of a mixture of china stone or petuntse and china clay, and is so hard that it cannot be filed. Soft paste has a warm, soft feeling when held in the hand, and can be marked with a file (but only by vandals).

Few examples of Lowestoft china are known to exist from the first few years of the manufactory, and the earliest dated pieces were made in 1761. At this time all decoration was in blue under the glaze, and the patterns were copied from the Chinese. The paste of these pieces is white and translucent, showing a greenish yellow by transmitted light ; the potting tends to be imperfect and the glaze speckled. From the outset, moulded patterns were extensively used, and some of the actual moulds were discovered on the site of the factory in the early years of this century, together with fragments of porcelain which have been invaluable in identifying doubtful productions.

The blued glaze gathered thickly in the footrims, at handle junctions, and at the upper edge of bowls, which were inverted for firing, and covered the whole article even to the inside of pot lids. A practice peculiar to Lowestoft was the painting of blue dashes, on occasion, at the junction of handles and spouts, in imitation of Nankin china. The footrims are triangular in section and are never undercut, and up to 1773 were sometimes, but not invariably, marked with a painter's number. These numbers were placed, almost without exception, inside the footrim and not on the base as at Bow. The numerals range from 1 to 30, and numbers up to 170 have been noted ; but it seems probable that the third digit in these cases may be an accidental brush stroke. The numbers 1 to 8 are common, with number 5 being most often seen ; this number is ascribed by tradition to Robert Allen, and number 3 to one Richard Phillips. These two are the only numbers to appear on the inscribed and dated pieces so popular at this factory, although it is thought that most of the ordinary underglaze blue painting was done by women.

A development of the inscribed mug or jug was the birth plaque, produced only at Lowestoft, a small, circular porcelain tablet usually about three inches in diameter, but rarely up to four-and-a-half inches, painted on the face with the name and date of birth of the child and on the reverse with a Chinese scene, floral spray or more rarely figures, a fox, or a sailing boat. Each plaque was pierced with one or two small holes for hanging, and only two or three years ago such a tablet was found hanging on the cottage wall of the great-granddaughter of the child for whom it was painted.

Powder-blue wares, similar to those produced at Bow, Worcester and Caughley, were popular between 1770 and 1780, the reserved panels being painted with Chinese scenes and flowers or, very rarely, with views of Lowestoft. In most cases the panels have ill-shaped wavy edges, but in others they follow the fan-shapes of their rival factories. During much the same period blue transfer-printed decoration was in fashion. A heavy dark blue 'willow pattern' was used, also rather coarse floral patterns and occasionally prints including a sportsman and his dog (after an engraving by Gamble, of Bungay) and 'Good Cross Chapel' (an ancient local place of worship). Additional painting in underglaze may be found on a transfer-printed piece.

Wares decorated in underglaze blue were produced at Lowestoft long after the other factories had generally forsaken it for the fashionable coloured china, and besides the more usual productions a wide variety of articles was made, including ink wells, pounce pots, paper weights, candlesticks, eye-baths, pap-warmers, feeding cups, and vases. In addition to the painters' numerals, which were not used after 1773, other marks were employed, notably the Worcester crescent, a small 'W,' Dresden crossed swords and, particularly in the case of dragon decoration, the letter 'V.'

In about 1774 enamel painting was introduced and for the remaining years of the factory's existence, polychrome wares were produced together with underglaze blue. The earliest attempts consisted of adding red enamel decoration to underglaze blue, producing the patterns attributed to the painter Redgrave and known as 'Root,' 'Dolls' House' and 'Two Bird.' Later, more elaborate enamel painting was introduced, using the palette peculiar to Lowestoft and including shades of pink, puce, brown and green, and painters like Thomas Rose and Thomas Curtis executed the patterns by which the factory is most commonly known, consisting of roses and other flowers, sometimes issuing out of a cornucopia, vase or basket, in conjunction with elaborate pink scale or lattice and festoon borders. Chinese figures are frequently to be found on tea services and other articles, and it has been said that their round East Anglian faces and Occidental

[71]

features disclose their source of origin. Very occasionally black pencilling was employed, sometimes heightened with gilt, or classical and floral patterns in pink camaieu or even German *hausmalerei* styles.

Undoubtedly the finest productions of the factory were the articles decorated between about 1774 and 1780 by the anonymous 'Tulip Painter,' who painted superb sprays of flowers, often including tulips and convolvulus, and the cylindrical mugs produced during the same period, sometimes in sets of three sizes, and finely painted with Chinese figures, local scenes or inscriptions.

Throughout the whole period from 1761 to 1799 souvenir pieces were produced in profusion, more than two hundred and twenty such pieces being known today. Sometimes the inscription consists of a name or names and date, sometimes it is 'A trifle from Lowestoft' or elsewhere, and occasionally it may incorporate a rhyme.

Although the figures described and illustrated by W. W. R. Spelman in his book *Lowestoft China* have been proved to be of Staffordshire origin, some small figures were made at Lowestoft including cats, deer, sheep, swans and *putti*. In the last category collectors still proudly produce vastly differing cherubs, and each swears to the Suffolk origin of his own child. Recent research has, however, established certain figures of musicians and *putti* beyond reasonable doubt.

A great deal of the continuing confusion about Lowestoft china emanates from the frequently quoted error on the part of Chaffers who, at the end of the last century, in his *Marks and Monograms on Pottery and Porcelain* broadcast the theory that the best products of the factory were painted on an Oriental body. It is now known beyond all doubt that no hard-paste porcelain was either made or decorated at the factory, but the fallacy gained so strong a hold in the world of ceramics, that to this day Chinese porcelain decorated with roses and other floral sprays, and with diaper or festoon borders in the style copied by the Lowestoft artists, is known to far too many as 'Oriental Lowestoft' or just 'Lowestoft.' If a coat of arms is included in the decoration the misnomer is even more firmly applied, although, in fact, very little armorial china is known to have been made at Lowestoft ; the best known examples are a tea-service made for the Revd. Robert Potter, Vicar of Lowestoft, another for Townshend of Honingham in Norfolk, and a third with the Ludlow crest, a mug with the arms of the Blacksmiths' Company, a jug with the arms of Monro of Bearcroft and a teapot with the arms of Barton.

Top left: inscribed coffee-pot painted with rural scenes, dated 1775. *Bottom left:* one of a unique pair of marriage mugs, *c.* 1780 (*W. E. Hatfield*). *Top right:* coffee-pot decorated by the Tulip Painter (*Noel Turner*). *Centre:* inscribed miniature teapot in the Curtis style, *c.* 1775 (*J. H. Nurse*). *Bottom right:* barrel-shaped trifle mug, and a rare tabby cat (*Paul Collection*)

On the left: a very early bell-shaped mug with runny-blue decoration *c.* 1760 (*Noel Turner*)

On the left: a rare coffee-pot with moulded floral decoration, *c.* 1765 (*Paul Collection*)

On the right: a rare Lowestoft jug with brick-coloured and gilt lattice ground (*Paul Collection*)

Top row: two early bell-shaped mugs dated 1767 and 1768 (*W. E. Hatfield*). *Centre row:* an early dragon bowl and a barrel-shaped teapot, *c.* 1770 (*Noel Turner*). *Bottom row:* an early miniature teapot, *c.* 1767, a unique mug inscribed with the name of a sailing vessel and dated 1772, and a birth plaque to Susan Golder, dated May 20, 1792 (*Noel Turner*)

In 1794 Robert Allen, who had started at the factory in 1757 at the age of twelve, commenced business as a stationer and china dealer, and with a small kiln decorated with local inscriptions pottery and porcelain produced elsewhere. This is not Lowestoft china. Neither are the hard white-paste fakes usually bearing a Trifle inscription, which came some years ago from the Paris factory of M. Samson and other Continental sources.

An apocryphal story exists blaming the downfall of the factory on the seizure, by Napoleon, of a ship carrying some £2,000 worth of porcelain to Holland ; but it seems probable that the real reason for the closing of the manufactory in 1802–3 was the change from wood to coal for firing, a change which gave distinct advantage to the Staffordshire potters. When it is remembered that both Chelsea and Bow had been transferred to Derby in the 1770's, and that the Longton Hall, Bristol and Plymouth factories had closed even earlier, it will be appreciated that Lowestoft at least outlived most of its rivals.

Today the number of important private collections of Lowestoft porcelain may be counted, if not quite on the fingers of one hand, most certainly on those of two ; although a larger number of more modest collectors have realized the charm of this very English china. Excellent collections may be seen at the Victoria and Albert Museum in London and the Castle Museum at Norwich, and a smaller collection at Christchurch Mansion, Ipswich.

Within the last few years two major collections have been dispersed, and a number of individual pieces of fine quality have also passed through the salerooms. Naturally, the highest prices are paid for the rare inscribed pieces, which may fetch anything from £40 to over £100. Similarly teapots, coffee-pots or mugs decorated by the 'Tulip Painter' will realize £50 or £60 each, compared with about half that price for examples by Rose or Curtis. A fine set of three mugs may be worth £200 to £300, whilst even a simple little birth plaque, of which only thirty-one are known, may well cost £50 if it is perfect. But, lest the amateur of slender means be deterred by these prices, it must be remembered that many delightful pieces of less importance may be bought for a very few pounds, and a cup and saucer nearly two hundred years old may still be acquired for only thirty shillings.

BETJEMAN'S BRITAIN

*An anthology of buildings
chosen & described by* JOHN BETJEMAN
and photographed for The Saturday Book
by EDWIN SMITH

THE BUILDINGS shown here, which date from the first half of this century back to the eleventh, all belong to another age. Today, when we build large blocks of flats, offices or factories we build more on the principles of setting up a marquee for a fête, that is to say we set up the essential struts as a skeleton and hang the walls off them like the curtains of a tent. The parts of large new buildings are mostly prefabricated, so that the chief job of an architect, when he is not filling in forms and complying with the regulations of local authorities, is assembling prefabricated parts in as pleasing patterns as he can devise from the standard patterns he finds in the catalogue. This is what modern architects call 'machine-made' architecture. I am not condemning it, though I think that at present far finer examples of it are to be found in America than in England. But I am not illustrating the style, because to put examples among the buildings shown here would be rather like introducing the latest types of motor car into an exhibition of post-chaises.

The buildings here represent 'hand-made' architecture, and are built from the ground up with their outside walls acting as their chief supports. They all imply a knowledge of masonry, of the carving of stone and wood, of the moulding of plaster and cast iron, and the knowledge, once common to all trained architects, of the Orders of Classical architecture (Composite, Corinthian, Ionic, Doric, etc.) and, in the case of Gothic architects, of mouldings and the centring of arches.

If one may make a rather dangerous generalization about the difference between Classic and Gothic architecture it is this. In Classical architecture you designed the outside first and fitted in the plan to conform with the façade. In Gothic architecture you made your plan first and that determined the appearance of the outside of the building. There are all sorts of exceptions to this generalization, just as there are exceptions to the current belief that all Gothic has pointed arches and all Classic has round ones. To take a literary parallel, Gothic architecture is rather like a poet using different metres to suit different moods, and Classic is rather like his trying to condense each mood into a sonnet.

The English buildings I have chosen are some of those I like, regardless of their date. Each is representative of a different phase of English 'hand-made' architecture. To those who object that there is an over-proportion of nineteenth-century buildings I would say : 'Look about you next time you go out of your house.' Most of the 'hand-made' buildings you will see belong to the last hundred years, when our population suddenly and alarmingly increased.

I think that these are some of the chief things to ask yourself about a building, whatever its age and style :—On its outside, how does it fit in with the landscape or with its neighbours in a street ? What is it built of, and do the materials suit the building itself and the district ? If there is decoration on the building is it well proportioned to the whole ? Are the windows too large or too small or just right in the wall space ? Are the panes of the windows well proportioned to the window itself ? Are the panels on doors in scale ? Are the mouldings around the building itself of a satisfactory size ? Is the roof at the right pitch or does it look like an ill-fitting hat ? Do the chimney stacks look like afterthoughts or do they seem to rest securely on the roof ? Has the designer considered the skyline ? And when you go into the building, does it show you at once what it is for ? Does it bring you to your knees if it is a church ? Does it, if it is a house, lead you on to explore further and suggest grander rooms beyond ? Does it lift you up if it is a public building ? Or make you feel at home if it is a small house ? Outside and in, is the building obviously what it was built to be ? And when you walk round it, is it truly three-dimensional ; that is to say, will it make a good sketch or Edwin Smith photograph inside or out from wherever you are standing ?

As to why one building is better than another—why, for instance, the Port of London Authority building near the Tower of London is a heavy mass of piled-up sculptured masonry, while the little arcaded memorial to the Merchant Seamen by Sir Edwin Lutyens which stands in front of it is infinitely grander and more satisfying—I can give no answer. I suppose it is that Lutyens was a great artist, and the architect of the Port of London Authority building was less of an artist.

Looking at buildings is just like looking at pictures or reading poetry or listening to music. It is something which demands discrimination. Discrimination only comes, when looking at architecture, from constantly using your eyes, if you have been born with an intuitive interest in your surroundings. Date and style have little to do with appreciation of architecture, though we all have our favourite dates and styles, which change as we develop. Finally, I don't think you can judge buildings *in vacuo* ; you have to consider them in terms of the purpose for which they were built and the social customs of their age. The public gallery of our villages and streets is always open, free for all.

I hope you will like some of the following exhibits from a small and extremely personal selection. From the Ritz to the Norman barons I shall show you some of my favourite buildings. If some of *your* favourites are left out this is not because I do not like them, but because there was not room and I wanted to show some of the lesser-known buildings among the more famous.

Opposite : ST MARY'S, WELLINGBOROUGH, 1904 onwards. *Architect and designer of all fittings, hangings and stained glass : Sir Ninian Comper.*

The latest and richest flowering of the Catholic Revival in The Church of England. Brown ironstone columns support white fan vaulting. The East End blazes with gold and red and blue. The idea of its builders was to bring beauty to the drab outskirts of a Midland manufacturing town.

The Ritz Hotel, London (Mewes and Davis)

Edwardian riches at their most elegant. A style which goes
with bridge, women and champagne and privilege. It
has a hint of Paris about it. The architects also designed
the Royal Automobile Club in Pall Mall. What a
contrast is this gilded international world of the south

St Andrew's, Roker Park, Co. Durham, 1906 (E. S. Prior)

with the rugged high-mindedness of the north of England. In this grand and solid church the lines of construction are severely shown. The woodwork and the stone tracery of the windows are solid and original. This church is born of the arts and crafts movement and is a Christian version of the aesthetic principles of William Morris.

Opposite : E. W. Bryan's Factory, Leicester, 1913 (S. Henry Langley)   *Above : Port Sunlight*

Messrs. Bryan's factory is an example of the enlightened industrial style where the building was unashamedly a factory and the architect emphasized its vertical lines of construction by subtle devices. The style goes with the Dryad Handicrafts and the work of Ernest Gimson (a Leicester man) and non-conformist benevolence. A similar spirit pervades Port Sunlight, started by the Lever Brothers in 1888. Like Bournville built by the Cadburys outside Birmingham and the Garden Village built by the Reckitts outside Hull, Port Sunlight provided cottages of local materials in local styles to house workers in a garden setting, and the factories, too, were to be surrounded by greenery as suggested by William Morris.

Annesley Lodge, Hampstead, 1895
(C. F. A. Voysey)

Work of each for weal of all ! Though the high-minded Liberal manufacturers hoped to make industrial England one leafy Bournville it was the middle classes who took more willingly to the idea. The small, detached house for artistic people of moderate income was first seen in the garden suburb of Bedford Park (1875), and by 1903 a whole city of such houses, each different, was invented by Ebenezer Howard for Letchworth. Architects in those days thought that they should also design fabrics and wallpapers and in the case of Mr Voysey everything for the house down to the very teaspoons and toast-racks. But the workers obstinately preferred the music hall to the folk mote and good old fair-ground baroque to homespuns and unstained oak. England's great contribution to Western architecture was, however, these small detached artistic houses in local styles. Their designers were the pupils of the great church builders of

Saloon bar,
Tabard Inn,
Bedford Park,
Chiswick, 1875
(R. Norman Shaw:
Tiles by William
de Morgan)

Lectern
inlaid with
mother-of-pearl
designed by
E. S. Prior for
St Andrew's,
Roker Park

Hampstead Garden City   *Below : Metropolitan Music Hall, Edgware Road, c. 1886*

St Bartholomew's, Brighton, 1874 (Edmund Scott)

the Tractarian Movement. If you had been a young architect in mid-Victorian times you would probably have been a high churchman and a voter for Mr Gladstone and your social conscience would have inspired you to build stately and original buildings in the slums so that the poor might have something in their neighbourhoods to uplift them. To this day the high church of a town is generally the one near the station. The great Victorian church builders did not copy medieval but went on, as they put it, where the Middle Ages left off, using modern materials and inventing styles of their own.

Right : St Augustine's, Kilburn, 1870–80 (J. L. Pears

t : The Law Courts, 1868–82 (G. E. Street)   Above : Town Hall, Manchester, 1868–77 (Alfred Waterhouse)

The new vigorous Gothic was not just used for churches. George Edmund Street, who designed the Law Courts, taught himself to be a smith, a joiner and a stained glass maker because he thought that an architect should also be master of all the crafts allied to building. He inspired the arts and crafts movement, and among his pupils were William Morris, Philip Webb and Norman Shaw.

The Coal Exchange, City of London, 1847–49 (J. B. Bunning)

So romantic, so convincingly old are the spires and towers of the Houses of Parliament that they are probably the most loved public buildings in the country, despite what goes on in them. The Victoria Tower seen here in contrast with the Buxton Memorial Fountain is my own favourite single part of this great group of buildings. The Georgian tradition of correct classical buildings went on right through the last century, as in the Coal Exchange. But if you were a young man in the 1840's, you would have thought Gothic progressive, and Classic a bit old-fashioned.

: *The Victoria Tower, Palace of Westminster, 1847–60 (Sir Charles Barry)*

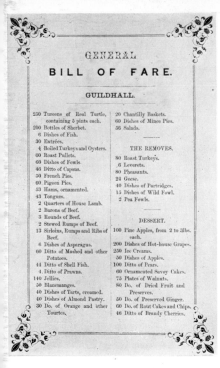

Lord Mayor's Banquet menu, 1856   *Victorian dining-room scene*

Opposite : the Lord Mayor's Banquet at the Guildhall, London, 1956

Seventeenth-century dining scene   *Eighteenth-century book of etiquette*

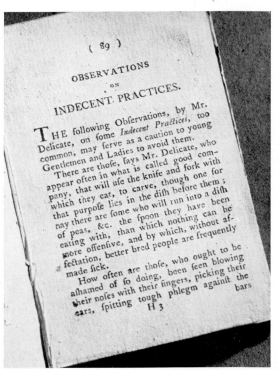

(89)

OBSERVATIONS
ON
INDECENT PRACTICES.

THE following Observations, by Mr. Delicate, on some *Indecent Practices*, too common, may serve as a caution to young Gentlemen and Ladies to avoid them.

There are those, says Mr. Delicate, who appear often in what is called good company, that will use the knife and fork with which they eat, to carve, though one for that purpose lies in the dish before them; nay there are some who will run into a dish of peas, &c. the spoon they have been eating with, than which nothing can be more offensive, and by which, without affectation, better bred people are frequently made sick.

How often are those, who ought to be ashamed of so doing, been seen blowing their noses with their fingers, picking their ears, spitting tough phlegm against the bars

H 3

The shape of Britain in Ptolemy's map of 1550 (Louis Meier) and the shape of Miss Julia St. George as Ariel are perhaps but artistic conjecture, though the lady's usefulness in the energetic curtain raiser leaves, in her case, room for doubt and hope.

Central Station, Newcastle-on-Tyne, 1850 (John Dobson)

The early Victorians, whether Gothic or Classic, had no fear of using cast iron, and civil engineers were still architects, and architects were not yet self-consciously artists who regarded engineers as 'practical' and insensitive. Bunning used cast iron moulded in the form of cables such as were used in coal mines for his grand rotunda in the Coal Exchange, London, and Dobson made the elegant roof of light cast iron blend happily with his severe and impressive main building of Newcastle Station.

Left : Interior of the Coal Exchange, London. Decorative panels by Sang

Early 19th-century Mill, Halifax.   *Above : Wharnecliffe Viaduct, Hanwell, 1838 (I. K. Brunel)*

The unconscious sense of scale shown by the builder of the mill on the opposite page (notice the larger windows on the ground floor and the relation of window to wall space above) is the survival of an innate sense of proportion which every builder seems to have possessed in the eighteenth century.   Brunel, like all great civil engineers, was an artist.   He favoured the Egyptian style in his youth, as at Clifton Suspension Bridge and in the Wharnecliffe Viaduct where he gives it Georgian proportions.   The flattish brick arches are his own.

Monkwearmouth Station, Durham, c. 1845 (John Dobson)

Splendour on top and squalor below in the industrial towns where the workers were as yet unprotected by the Factory Act. But what real splendour on top ! Monkwearmouth station was the terminus of the line before it crossed the river. It was built when people were proud of railways and when, quite rightly they thought they beautified the landscape. Dobson's design is on the early principle of railway stations, where the platforms were mere sheds and the waiting room was a huge public building where passengers sat until the train was announced.

The early Victorian terrace such as that at Pennsylvania Park, Exeter, was designed to show up sunlight and shadow by means of shallow grooves and light iron work and pale paint on the plaster. The people who lived in such terraces as these were probably as unaware of conditions in the growing industrial north as the characters in Jane Austen seem to have been unaware of the Napoleonic Wars.

> The day was fair, the cannon roar'd,
>   Cold blew the bracing north,
> And Preston's Mills, by thousands, pour'd
>   Their little captives forth.

Ebenezer Elliott might just as well have been writing of Halifax, instead of Preston.

nsylvania Park, Exeter, c. 1840.   Below : Halifax, Yorks, with a well proportioned cast-iron lamp standard

Above : The Mausoleum, Brocklesby Park, Lincs, 1787–94 (James Wyatt)
Opposite : Tombs of the Pelham family inside the Mausoleum, Brocklesby
Below : The Bridge, Tyringham, Bucks, 1793–c. 1800 (Sir John Soane)

Go back from the Industrial Age to the Classical one, to that brief period in our history, from Tudor to the nineteenth century, when most of the great country houses were built. Not only were the houses part of the landscape, but their adjuncts such as temples, bridges and lodges and clumps of trees were designed to turn the country into a moving classical landscape as the traveller by chaise went visiting. Man commemorated himself in the Age of Reason with the best sculpture : churches and mausolea generally contain works of art to the memory of local landowners.

: St James's, Garlickhithe, 1676–83. Above : St Mary-at-Hill, 1670–1676 (both, Sir Christopher Wren)

Merchants in cities still had the tradition of the medieval guilds. The great Wren churches, sometimes Gothic and sometimes Renaissance (St Paul's Cathedral is a Renaissance building with a medieval plan), were the joint efforts of citizens. They sat in cedar-scented pews, summoned from their shops and halls by the tinkle of Anglican steeples.

The Manor House, Finstock, Oxon. Early seventeenth century

When it was no longer necessary to fortify your house, if you were a local lord, against your neighbours, when farmers and merchants began to prosper from the wool trade and when the great abbeys ceased to be the chief landlords, men displayed their wealth in their private houses. They built houses for their families instead of houses of God. All over England there are charming small manor houses in local materials, whether it be stone or timber, and the best are in the limestone villages, generally near the church and walled off from the cottages. The richest and most powerful Elizabethans delighted in huge glazed windows where their forebears had had to put up with the thick walls of castles. The festal light of candles shone on tapestry and fine Spanish chairs. English cherubs and carved fruit and capitals showed in wood, stone and plaster the Tudor and Elizabethan delight in the new-found knowledge, already firmly established on the Continent, of the ancient architecture of Rome and Italy.

The last phase of Medieval Gothic in England, known as Perpendicular, gave the stained glass artist his great chance, for the walls were almost of glass and the vaulted stone roofs were designed to have their weight carried by strong buttresses between the windows. Thus the grandest examples, clearly the work of architects and not

ardwick Hall, Derbyshire, 1591–97.   Overleaf : New Building, Peterborough Cathedral, 1438–96

merely local builders, were like enormous marquees whose supports were the buttresses and whose curtained walls were glass held in position by carved and traceried stone. These masterpieces had a proportion of their own, and were a unity of colour and sculpture and construction which, with the aid of music and a religious ceremony with vested priests, transported man from this world to the next.

King's College Chapel, Cambridge, 1446–1515. Screen and stalls, 1532–35. Organ 1606

Peterborough Cathedral, West Front, 1200–20. Porch, c. 1370. Opposite : Patrington Church, Yorks, c.

In Medieval England the abbeys first created architectural styles. Here were the men of art, while the soldiers lived in castles. The West Front of the Benedictine abbey of Peterborough has long seemed to me one of the most daring creations of the Middle Ages —that detached west wall with its great hollow spaces and the narrow opening in the middle. A later generation of monastic architects had the courage to set down in the midst of this design that jewel-like porch in an utterly contrasting style which yet does not interfere with the main design but enhances it.

Most village churches are buildings rather than architecture. But here and there are village churches which are all-of-a-piece. Patrington, which sails like a galley over the flat landscape of Holderness, is an example.

Size is not the secret of great architecture, proportion has more to do with it, and the texture of time adds another quality. The Chapel of St John in the White Tower, in the City of London, 1080–88, is, to me, one of the most perfect small buildings.

"Fayre Fulgay"

SOME ACCOUNT OF THE HISTORY, AMENITIES AND ARCHITECTURAL GEMS OF

* * FULGAY * *

The Official Handbook of Fulgay

PUBLISHED BY:

The Fulgay & West Rumset Chamber of Commerce

IN ASSOCIATION WITH

FULGAY URBAN DISTRICT COUNCIL

I—S B

FAYRE FULGAY

Foreword

It affords me singular pleasure to wish 'bon voyage,' as it were, to this new and entirely revised edition of *Fair Fulgay* which has the added distinction of being the first 'Official Guide' to appear in *The Saturday Book*. I should like to thank the Editor for giving his readers this exceptional opportunity of getting to know our ancient town which unfailingly extends a warm welcome to the holidaymaker, the potential resident, and the businessman in need of expansion alike. For not only do we of Fulgay enjoy a goodly heritage from the past, but we are also a progressive community fully conscious of the challenge of this Modern Age in which we are called upon to reside. I understand that *Fair Fulgay* has been chosen as a 'typical example of local enterprise and local lore,' and while I and my fellow Fulgarians not unnaturally like to think of our town as 'sui generis' rather than actually 'typical,' I am confident that all who peruse these pages that follow will swiftly perceive that while Fulgay richly deserves her traditional soubriquet of 'Fair' she is also undeniably 'Forward' as well.

John Foster White

Chairman of the Fulgay Urban District Council.

FAYRE FULGAY

Fair Fulgay thou art of Rumset towns I wean,
With mart and stream and steeple ever more the Quean.

Thus wrote a Georgian rector, the Reverend Hosiah Bawdle, author of *Reflections Upon The Rheumatick Condition* and other works well worthy of more detailed study, and the words of this local bard still ring every bit as true today as of yore. Fulgay is of immemorial antiquity. In Domesday it is generally identified with 'Vulghareinges' as being a place with pasture sufficient for six swine, and through the centuries it has remained the busy hub of a rich farming area.

WHY FULGAY ? The exact meaning of the name is not known, though the termination '-gay' usually signifies an island and the water meadows surrounding the town suggest that it may at times have been completely severed from the rest of Rumset. Local residents were, indeed, reminded of this historic isolation when the River Fulge broke its banks following the phenomenal spring tides of 1938, 1939, 1942, 1947, 1951, 1955, and other years. A more picturesque explanation of the name, however, derives from the traditional belief that Queen Elizabeth I once visited the town during one

The phenomenal spring tide of 1939

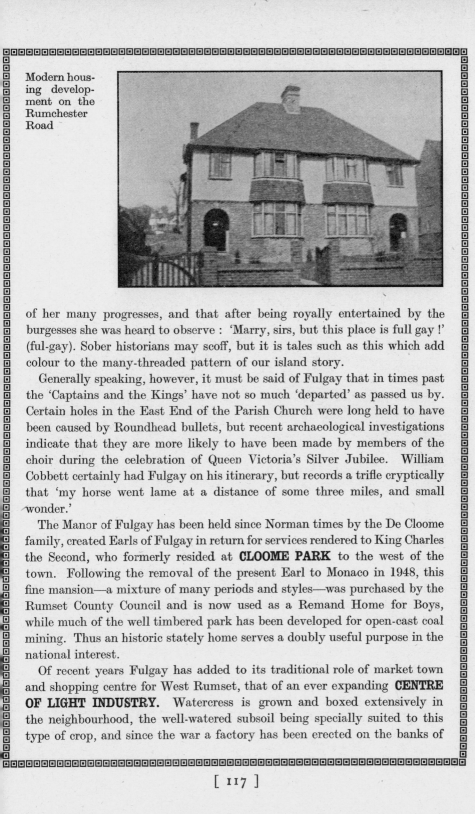

Modern housing development on the Rumchester Road

of her many progresses, and that after being royally entertained by the burgesses she was heard to observe : 'Marry, sirs, but this place is full gay !' (ful-gay). Sober historians may scoff, but it is tales such as this which add colour to the many-threaded pattern of our island story.

Generally speaking, however, it must be said of Fulgay that in times past the 'Captains and the Kings' have not so much 'departed' as passed us by. Certain holes in the East End of the Parish Church were long held to have been caused by Roundhead bullets, but recent archaeological investigations indicate that they are more likely to have been made by members of the choir during the celebration of Queen Victoria's Silver Jubilee. William Cobbett certainly had Fulgay on his itinerary, but records a trifle cryptically that 'my horse went lame at a distance of some three miles, and small wonder.'

The Manor of Fulgay has been held since Norman times by the De Cloome family, created Earls of Fulgay in return for services rendered to King Charles the Second, who formerly resided at **CLOOME PARK** to the west of the town. Following the removal of the present Earl to Monaco in 1948, this fine mansion—a mixture of many periods and styles—was purchased by the Rumset County Council and is now used as a Remand Home for Boys, while much of the well timbered park has been developed for open-cast coal mining. Thus an historic stately home serves a doubly useful purpose in the national interest.

Of recent years Fulgay has added to its traditional role of market town and shopping centre for West Rumset, that of an ever expanding **CENTRE OF LIGHT INDUSTRY.** Watercress is grown and boxed extensively in the neighbourhood, the well-watered subsoil being specially suited to this type of crop, and since the war a factory has been erected on the banks of the River Fulge for the manufacture of a famous brand of detergent. Hence our local stream is now sometimes spoken of in jocular fashion as the 'Foamy Fulge!' There is also a flourishing stearine works in the town.

Our climate is exceptional for an inland town, for although some thirteen miles from the coast the intervening gentle undulations of Fulgay Fen— a stretch of green untouched by the hand of man—allow us full access to the vigorous sea breezes which sweep in boisterously from the north-east.

A WALK ROUND FULGAY. Let us start from the new bus station of the Rumset National Road Car and Omnibus Traction Company from

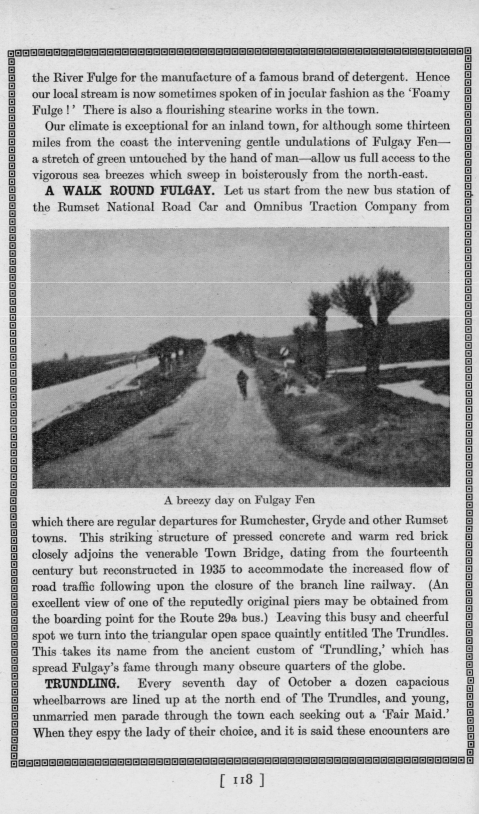

A breezy day on Fulgay Fen

which there are regular departures for Rumchester, Gryde and other Rumset towns. This striking structure of pressed concrete and warm red brick closely adjoins the venerable Town Bridge, dating from the fourteenth century but reconstructed in 1935 to accommodate the increased flow of road traffic following upon the closure of the branch line railway. (An excellent view of one of the reputedly original piers may be obtained from the boarding point for the Route 29a bus.) Leaving this busy and cheerful spot we turn into the triangular open space quaintly entitled The Trundles. This takes its name from the ancient custom of 'Trundling,' which has spread Fulgay's fame through many obscure quarters of the globe.

TRUNDLING. Every seventh day of October a dozen capacious wheelbarrows are lined up at the north end of The Trundles, and young, unmarried men parade through the town each seeking out a 'Fair Maid.' When they espy the lady of their choice, and it is said these encounters are not invariably fortuitous, they leave their fellows and approach her with these time-honoured words : 'Be thou my fair maid and I will trundle' ee.' If the 'Fair Maid' be willing, she replies : 'Right readily I'll be thy trundly, for weal or for woe.' The young man then hands her a 'posy' of freshly gathered cress and seats her in one of the barrows. When all are thus 'beauteously' occupied, the 'swains' race their 'fair maids' three times round The Trundles. In olden days the winners received three freshly baked Trundle cakes (a local delicacy) and a length of 'fair, coarse linen,' but in

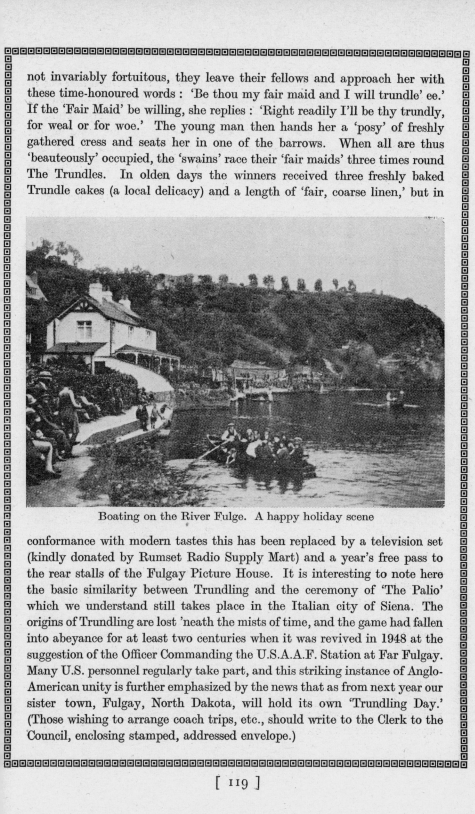

Boating on the River Fulge. A happy holiday scene

conformance with modern tastes this has been replaced by a television set (kindly donated by Rumset Radio Supply Mart) and a year's free pass to the rear stalls of the Fulgay Picture House. It is interesting to note here the basic similarity between Trundling and the ceremony of 'The Palio' which we understand still takes place in the Italian city of Siena. The origins of Trundling are lost 'neath the mists of time, and the game had fallen into abeyance for at least two centuries when it was revived in 1948 at the suggestion of the Officer Commanding the U.S.A.A.F. Station at Far Fulgay. Many U.S. personnel regularly take part, and this striking instance of Anglo-American unity is further emphasized by the news that as from next year our sister town, Fulgay, North Dakota, will hold its own 'Trundling Day.' (Those wishing to arrange coach trips, etc., should write to the Clerk to the Council, enclosing stamped, addressed envelope.)

The greensward in the centre of The Trundles has lately been laid out in the most tasteful manner as a **GARDEN OF REST,** with an ornamental fish pond and winding paths of crazy paving. This necessitated the felling of five large old oak trees, which formerly occupied the site and were known as 'The Watch Committee.' Sentimentalists may mourn their passing, but there is no denying that without their shady vigilance The Trundles is a lighter, brighter and much tidier place.

To the north of The Trundles looms Fulgay's greatest glory—the Parish Church, for the following informative notes on which we are indebted to the Rector, the Reverend Canon F. S. A. Cox-Camden, a Past President of the Rumset Archaeological Society and Field Sports Institute.

THE PARISH CHURCH. There may well have been a place of worship at Fulgay in Saxon Times (Bede clxviii) but if so nothing is known of it. The first definite reference occurs in the Court Rolls of the Manor for 1232 (*Notes and Queries*, Vol. MM.), which specifically speak of 'ecclesia' (a church). The list of rectors, however, does not commence until 1307 when Humfrey de Lyttletone took office (ibid. xl, vi, vii). According to legend this Humfrey was formerly a minstrel much given to affirming 'I praye as I doe please,' but there is no authority for this whatsoever. As to the ancient fane itself, the dedication of which is unknown, it is believed that the core of the third pillar from the W. of the S. arcade may embody Trans. work, but plainly the church was wholly rebuilt in the fourteenth century so that it is primarily Decorated and Perpendicular (V.C.H. IV, 266a). Since that time our parish church has remained basically unchanged, i.e., it still comprises Tower of three stages, surmounted by a crocketed spire (last rebuilt after being destroyed by lightning in 1864), nave with N. and S. aisles, choir with N. and S. chapels. It was vigorously restored by Sir Gilbert Scott in 1857 and again under the personal direction of the Fifth Earl of Fulgay (a noted eccentric of whom many amusing anecdotes are extant) in 1883. As a result the interior is perhaps lacking in many visible signs of antiquity, but the following should be noted : (1) N. of S. chapel square recess, possibly an aumbry ; (2) floor of S. chapel brass to unknown priest, much defaced and unfortunately now hidden by the organ ; (3) N.E. corner of nave, fragmentary wall-painting, subject unknown, first discerned during repairs to damp-course ; (4) N. porch, rudely incised stone slab raised from the bed of the Fulge in 1923. It is hoped to bring further points of similarly great antiquarian interest to light when the church is once more restored. This is a matter of grave urgency, and all visitors are enjoined to help by becoming members of 'The Friends of Fulgay Church.' Enrolment forms and deeds of covenant will be found on the font cover. *N.B.* The Tower may be ascended (at own risk) by arrangement with the Verger. Adults :

6d., children under fourteen, 3d. ; special reductions for parties of twenty or more on written application to the Rector. A small fee is also charged for the rubbing of brasses. When locked, key to south door may be obtained from Mrs Colls, Church Cottage, 3 Trundles Lane.

Our Parish Church

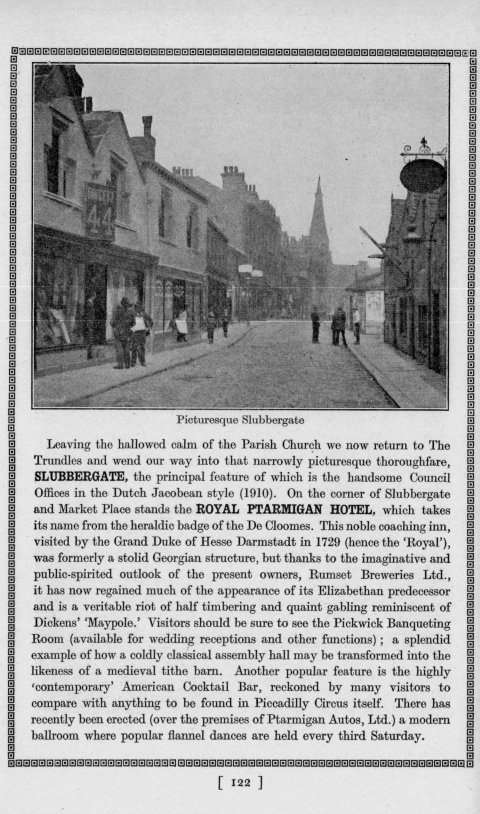

Picturesque Slubbergate

Leaving the hallowed calm of the Parish Church we now return to The Trundles and wend our way into that narrowly picturesque thoroughfare, **SLUBBERGATE,** the principal feature of which is the handsome Council Offices in the Dutch Jacobean style (1910). On the corner of Slubbergate and Market Place stands the **ROYAL PTARMIGAN HOTEL,** which takes its name from the heraldic badge of the De Cloomes. This noble coaching inn, visited by the Grand Duke of Hesse Darmstadt in 1729 (hence the 'Royal'), was formerly a stolid Georgian structure, but thanks to the imaginative and public-spirited outlook of the present owners, Rumset Breweries Ltd., it has now regained much of the appearance of its Elizabethan predecessor and is a veritable riot of half timbering and quaint gabling reminiscent of Dickens' 'Maypole.' Visitors should be sure to see the Pickwick Banqueting Room (available for wedding receptions and other functions); a splendid example of how a coldly classical assembly hall may be transformed into the likeness of a medieval tithe barn. Another popular feature is the highly 'contemporary' American Cocktail Bar, reckoned by many visitors to compare with anything to be found in Piccadilly Circus itself. There has recently been erected (over the premises of Ptarmigan Autos, Ltd.) a modern ballroom where popular flannel dances are held every third Saturday.

FULGAY MARKET is held every Tuesday, and in a fast changing world it continues to reflect the abiding life of the countryside. The stalls offer a wide variety of merchandise ranging from second-hand articles of clothing to jewellery, antique silver, kitchenware, etc. The cries of the vendors, many of whom travel here from as far afield as Whitechapel, Leeds and Birmingham, add a colourful touch to the proceedings. On the left of the Market Place is the **OLD CORN EXCHANGE,** erected by public subscription in 1887 and much admired by connoisseurs of Ruskinesque Gothic. It is now used as a Civic Entertainments Centre and also houses the Fulgay branch of the Rumset County Libraries (open Wednesday and Saturday 2 to 4 p.m.). Among the many functions which take place here are the productions of the **FULGAY AMATEUR DRAMATIC AND LIGHT OPERA SOCIETY.** This body does much to enliven those long winter evenings, and shows great versatility and originality in its choice of pieces. In recent years, for instance, it has given us such notable West End successes as *George and Margaret, Quiet Wedding, Dear Octopus,* and from the Continent, Strindberg's *Life With Father.* Always looking to the future the Light Opera section has already resolved to stage the first Rumset production of *My Fair Lady.* In the meantime, they are currently rehearsing their sixth revival of *Mercenary Mary,* always a great favourite with Fulgay audiences.

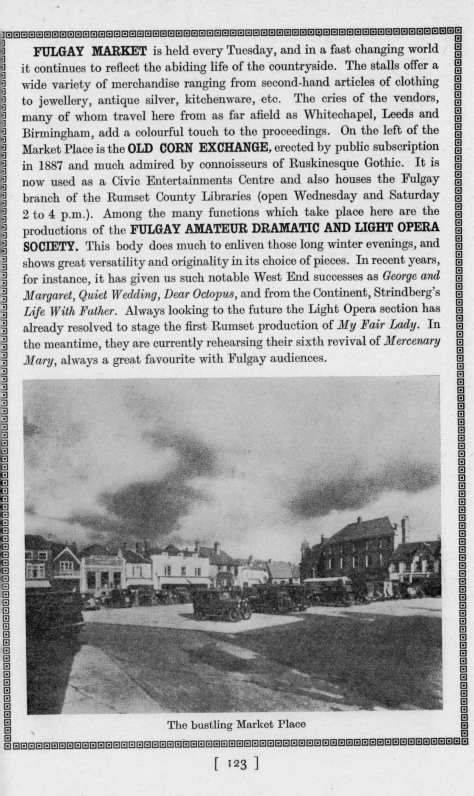

The bustling Market Place

High Street—centre of commerce

But we must dally no more in the haunts of Thespis, turning instead to the **HIGH STREET,** the hub of Fulgay's commercial life, where we may readily see fresh evidence that the town does not lag behind its larger brothers. All the leading stores are represented, easily identified by their familiar and distinctive fascias, as are the 'Big Five' banks and three major building societies. There are also several old-established local concerns dealing in ironmongery, drapery, etc. At the east end of High Street where the Iron Bridge (designed and given to the town by the Fifth Earl of Fulgay—see under Parish Church) crosses the disused branch railway line, we come to the **WEST RUMSET COUNTY SECONDARY SCHOOL FOR BOYS** which was, until the passing of the Education Act, known by the somewhat cumber-

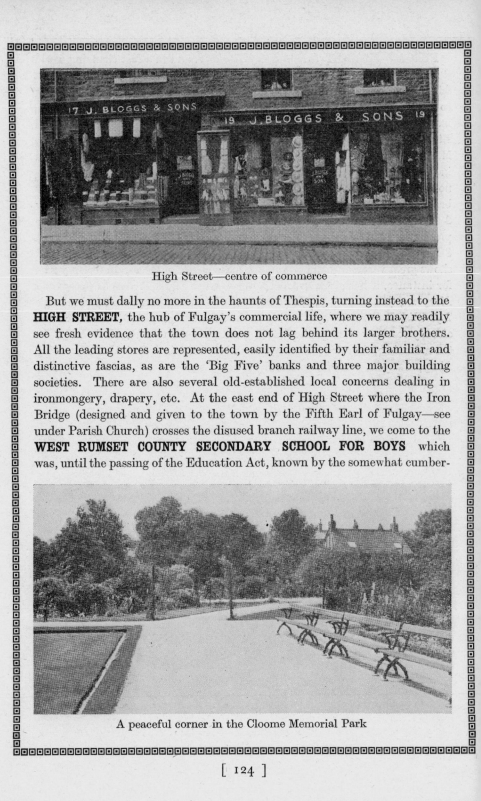

A peaceful corner in the Cloome Memorial Park

some title of Lady Athalia de Cloome's Free Grammar School of God's Providence. Although the school is now housed in fine modern premises of the 'functional' type, the original Tudor schoolroom is still preserved as an ante-natal clinic.

Retracing our steps once more we can either turn left to visit the **CLOOME MEMORIAL PARK** and **MUNICIPAL SPORTS GROUND**, offering a fine display of geraniums in season, or else proceed to the western extremity of High Street where it merges into the Rumchester Road. Here are signs of Fulgay's growing popularity as a place of residence ; chief among them being

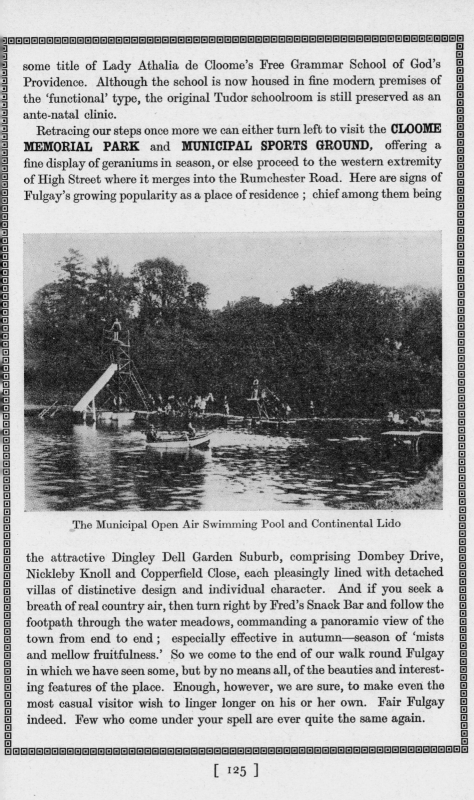

The Municipal Open Air Swimming Pool and Continental Lido

the attractive Dingley Dell Garden Suburb, comprising Dombey Drive, Nickleby Knoll and Copperfield Close, each pleasingly lined with detached villas of distinctive design and individual character. And if you seek a breath of real country air, then turn right by Fred's Snack Bar and follow the footpath through the water meadows, commanding a panoramic view of the town from end to end ; especially effective in autumn—season of 'mists and mellow fruitfulness.' So we come to the end of our walk round Fulgay in which we have seen some, but by no means all, of the beauties and interesting features of the place. Enough, however, we are sure, to make even the most casual visitor wish to linger longer on his or her own. Fair Fulgay indeed. Few who come under your spell are ever quite the same again.

The spacious new ballroom of the historic Royal Ptarmigan Hotel

Sport and Recreation

GOLF : A nine-hole course has been laid down by Plunket's Pasture on the banks of the Fulge and holiday visitors are welcomed. The Professional, Greenkeeper and Herdsman, Mr. J. Rundle, is in attendance and will be pleased to arrange hire of equipment. (23a bus to Widgeon Lane and then 10 minutes brisk walk.)

ANGLING : Good coarse fishing in the Fulge (apply for permit to Sales Manager, Fulge Detergents Ltd.), but present industrial conditions not always favourable. **BOWLS, CROQUET** and **TENNIS** (one hard court) provided for at Cloome Memorial Park.

CINEMA : The Picture House, High Street, erected in 1925, seats 500 and offers the latest cinematographic productions from leading British and American studios. Performances Monday to Friday, 6.15 and 8.40. Matinées

Tuesday and Thursday, 2.45 ; Saturday continuous from 2.45. In addition to those already mentioned in 'A Walk Round Fulgay,' the town possesses flourishing societies devoted to philately, bird-watching, aero-modelling, theosophy, etc.

EARLY CLOSING : Thursday. **CAR PARK :** Railway Approach (10 minutes brisk walk from Market Place). **Rates,** 1957–58 : 28s. 6d. in the £.

POPULATION : 4,331.

LOCAL NEWSPAPER : *The Fulgay and West Rumset Advertiser*, with which is incorporated the *Fulgay Weekly Intelligencer*. Published Fridays, 3d.

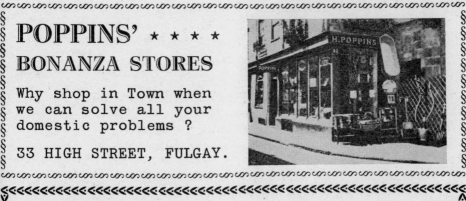

DORSET NOON

by SARA JACKSON

Shut your eyes ;
There is cowparsley at your feet,
And all the drowsy, blowzy heat
Of buttercup fields made vaguely neat
By hedgerows where wild roses meet
To blush or bleach above the seat
A fallen stump has made for lovers,
Who know no time but one heart-beat
This dragonflyed, shade-lazy day
When cloud-ships leave their ocean blue
To hoist up sail on trees of may.

Open your ears
To music of a gossamer air,
Enchanted utterly, and rare ;
Drunken with self-delight ; more fair
Than all those personal songs that dare
To add to this imperial glare
Of gold caught up to greater gold ;
Where only the poppy's harlot blare
Of syncopation bars off lark
From grasshopper as they conspire
To orchestrate against the dark.

Now, fall asleep !
For night with an essential breeze
Makes solemn and immobile trees
Shake into laughter as they tease,
Leaf against leaf, a tune to please
The pale, bewildered Pleides
That half afraid of heavenly wealth,
Swarm like a crowd of wistful bees
Above the earth we love or curse,
Trapped in its unrelenting maze,
Alone, for better or for worse.

MARSEILLES REVISITED

by TUDOR EDWARDS

CONVENTIONAL travellers, in their headlong rush to the Riviera, are apt to regard Marseilles as a population centre which congests the western end of the Provençal littoral, or, at best, as the herald of the true south. No more, perhaps, than that. Yet Marseilles is one of the cities of excitement, with a quality of unreality, an atmosphere so charged with visions of sin and violence overflowing from novels by Simenon and Pierre MacOrlan, and from films by Marcel Pagnol, that the place seems grossly fictitious.

Even one's introduction is dramatic, whether arriving at the station, terraced high upon a stone staircase plunging deep into the city, or hovering by plane over the desolate bushland of the Camargue, the Etang de Berre and the huddle of Martigue. There is nothing fictitious, however, about the trams screaming up and down the Canebière for twenty hours a day ; and Marseilles is among the noisiest towns in Europe. The second city in France, it is no more French than Naples is Italian. It is a city of the Levant. Scholars maintain that Greek was spoken in Marseilles up to the sixth century. The sixth century ? Up to the Great War the fishermen of the *quartier St-Jean* had a substantial vocabulary of purely Greek terms incidental to their calling, and much of it is still spoken.

Despite its long history, however, Marseilles is largely a creation of the Second Empire. The Canebière has the air, if not exactly the quality, of the Champs-Elysées, and its women are almost equally *soignée*. Everywhere is the spontaneous gaiety and humour of the expansive Marseillaise, for this is the city of Honoré Daumier, the caricaturist of bourgeois society, and of Edmond Rostand, the neo-Romantic who in his play *Cyrano de Bergerac* raised the ridiculous to the sublime. Shops, kiosks and flower markets sparkle with Gallic artistry, and from the cafés comes always the music of that quick, French, quite impossible two-step, or Tino Rossi wailing *Souviens-toi ?* One ventures into quieter side streets—the Rue St-Ferréol with its pastrycook shops, the Rue du Paradis where is Flammarion's delightful bookshop, the Rue St-Barbe with its Arab quarter, the Rue de Rome with its Sunday morning food stalls heaped with all kinds of *charcuterie* and such Marseillais specialities as the *pissaladeira* (a mixture of onions stewed in oil, spread on bread and baked, and garnished with anchovies and black olives).

Architecturally, the city is not exciting. The heavy hand of the Second Empire has throttled the principal buildings, the Palais Longchamps, the Musée des Beaux-Arts, the mock-Byzantine Cathedral and the basilica of Notre-Dame de la Garde, all pretentious buildings of doubtful taste, and most of them by one man, the ubiquitous Henri Esperandieu. One comes unexpectedly upon some of these buildings, and there are vistas which have a Piranesi quality, but the drama fades as one approaches to find the detail dead and clumsy. The Bourse of 1860 is easily the best of this period. There are a few town houses of the *grand siècle*, and the former Hôtel de Ville is in a mild Baroque, neglected and hidden away like a Cinderella in the Vieux Port. The one building of real merit is the Château Borely, beautifully balanced and proportioned, near the edge of the sea, its park, which once was graced by the elegant Empress Eugénie, now swarming with the *petit peuple* scuttling between the bathing cabins and the restaurants.

But Marseilles is not a city merely and cannot be measured in terms of bricks and mortar. It is a state of mind, an experience, a heyday in the blood. It is useless to pretend that the Vieux Port is what it was, though Marseilles is recovering its pre-war shipping and it is still pre-eminently a melting-pot of the Mediterranean. Before the war one could sail away to Paul Gauguin's Tahiti for £25, and even today you can escape to Algiers or Tunis for as little as £3. The notice board outside the Messageries Maritimes is a signpost to the ends of the earth. In the Foyer du Marin, the seamen's mission near the docks, Père Bethaz tends the tropical garden and its exotic flowers brought back by French sailors from the Cameroons and the East Indies.

Time was when Marseilles was reputed to be the most wicked city under the sun. The Germans, paradoxically enough, were largely instrumental in cleaning it up when they destroyed the sordid huddle of labyrinthine streets on one side of the Vieux Port. Today this quarter is dominated by Le Corbusier's block of flats, the *Unité d'habitation*, tethered to the ground by enormous concrete stilts. This is the new Marseilles, as tidy and respectable as a synthetic cheese. The bawdy Rabelaisian life of the Marseilles I knew is gone. . . .

It was the winter of 1938–39. In the cafés the hum of conversation reached a hysterical pitch ; there was so much talk of peace that war was almost inevitable. Only two days ago Neville Chamberlain had returned to London from Munich. There was both tension and crispness in the air as my friend and I, newly landed from a P. and O. boat in which we were working our passages to India, walked along the Canebière. Marseilles was new to me, but not to Jimmy, the adventurer, and it was Jimmy's Marseilles that I was now to see—the Marseilles of harlots and *souteneurs*, of confidence men fawning over tea in the Hôtel de Noailles, of seamen's clubs in the dock area, of the British and American Bar in the Place de la Bourse with its palms and shuttered windows, of squalid *estaminets* in the purlieus of the Rue de la République, where one got drunk in the middle of the afternoon with frowsy doxies tugging insistently at one's elbow and promising all manner of unmentionable delights. For this was a city where pleasure was confounded with vice, where night belonged to the Devil.

We entered a monstrous world of formidable novelties. At last even Jimmy had had enough. Jimmy was not vicious, he was simply oozing with adolescent vitality, hungry for life, and he had springs of courage which were to gain him the Military Cross before he fell in Normandy. We vowed to dedicate our remaining days and nights to the things of mind and spirit, if indeed these existed in Marseilles. Thus it was that we passed one night through the Ionic portico of the Opéra to see *L'Arlésienne*. The theatre was only half full, yet company and audience managed to instil some shock of electricity into the building, for the theatre is so much more in French than in English bones. The play, for it is virtually a play with music, had a hothouse atmosphere, so charged was it with drama, and the audience wildly cheered Bizet's brilliant music for encore after encore. . . .

Where the Vieux Port used to be, there is nothing now to speak for the past. A new Marseilles has taken shape, perhaps more respectable than the sordid city I had known, but also perhaps less human. Yet there is still mystery and colour. On the other side of the Vieux Port the restaurants are alive with lights, with turning spits, spattering and coiling before the blowing charcoal, with copper casseroles burnished like the sun, and the sweet aromatic scent of spices and stuffing mingling with the pirouetting smoke of Havanas and *Gauloises*. The Coca-Cola régime may have succeeded in territorial ambitions which far outstrip those of Hitler and Stalin, but in Marseilles the café is still regarded as an adjunct to conversation and to digestion. Here the voluble Marseillaise will be found to be shrewd, humorous, essentially civilized, and far from being the suspicious, sordid and narrow characters, somewhat inarticulate, with little knack of expressing themselves except through the ballot-box, of Zola's characters. Here you can eat food delectable in its simplicity, or you can matriculate at will among the mysterious sea foods of the Mediterranean.

The fish stalls on the quays are laden with such a strange variety that one is reminded of the catalogue of fish in the fourth book of Rabelais' *Pantagruel*. They are all here—the sea-snails, pipe-fish, the heraldic-looking seahorse, the tuberous sea-squirts locally known as *violettes de mer*, *praires* or small clams, *loup de rocher* (which Ford Madox Ford called 'the most radiant, the most delicate and the most costly of all the fishes of all the seas and rivers that God has made'), *moulets*, *sards*, *canadelles* and *gobis* (these make excellent soup), *grondin*, or red gurnet, eels, lampreys, mussels and oysters, lobsters and shrimps and a few score more, not least of which is the *rascasse*. This venomous little beast has nearly a score of fangs, and the fishermen who suffer from its poisonous prickles call it the Scorpion or the Sea-Devil.

The *rascasse* is the chief ingredient of the fish-stew common to this region, the *bouillabaisse*, a truly Homeric dish which in some households hereabouts must only be made by the men, though the women naturally share it. Though Thackeray sang of it long ago, this is still an adventure of the palate for most English travellers. Briefly, it consists of various fish, including the indispensable *rascasse*, swiftly being browned in olive oil with chopped onions, tomatoes, garlic, saffron, fennel and those fragrant herbs and spices which recall the sun-baked hills of Provence, then being quickly boiled under water, and finally served on a layer of toasted bread. The saffron colour of this dish of mystery is obtained from the saffron itself (the dried anthers of crocus flowers) and from the *rascasse*. It is obtainable in most Marseilles restaurants, but to be certain of the real thing one should go to Isnard's, where the chef Isnard has reigned supreme in the kitchen for over forty years, Pascal's, which has now passed from father to son, the Au Filet de Sole, traditionally visited by the President of the Republic whenever he is in Marseilles, or the Mont Ventous, with its *poisson grillé au fenouil*.

Both the tang of the Mediterranean and the hot scent of Africa are borne into the open restaurants of the Vieux Port, where traces of early civilization survive in the kitchens. Here you will find *la poutargue*, a dish of hard caviare of eggs and grey mullet which was known to the Cretan fishermen under King Minos. There is octopus *sauté* with tomatoes, white wine, rosemary, laurel, garlic and parsley. There is the fish known as *loup* grilled upon a bed of fennel and *flambé* with Armagnac. And on the eve of Christmas *la raïto*, a dish of flavoured spiced eels, may be eaten just as it was by the Greeks on the eve of winter.

Of a rather limited selection of hotels the most elegant, and the most astronomically priced, are La Reserve on the slope of a great hill scented with green *maquis*, the ducal Hôtel de Noaille and the Grand. One drinks these days at the Cintre Bar off the Canebière, but there are numerous night-clubs. The latter are thriving, and one night-club owner now lives in the Provençal château of Vauvenargues. The Marseillaise are a prosperous people (the fabulous local black market during the war created many *nouveaux riches*) and they are familiar with the violence of sudden wealth and the decline of intelligence into sophistry. They have long had a reputation for being spendthrift. Until about the time of the Great War many small middle-class families would think nothing of squandering a half-year's savings on a breakfast at Roubion's.

The little Satap buses spring off regularly for the fishing villages of Martigues and Cassis. In Martigues, houses with pastel-shaded stuccoed fronts flaking into filigree stand at the water's edge. Here the great tunny fish are netted. There is jousting by the local fishermen, and night fishing by flare light, when one hunts the octopus with the *foene* or spear. With goggles and frog-flippers you can hunt all manner of gleaming, brightly coloured fish darting above waving and undulating plants of fantastic shape. This is a deadly serious sport, but hardly more serious than underwater exploration in the Bay of Fos, where the ruins of an old Greek colony can still be seen. Afterwards, relaxation at the Hôtel Ste-Anne, where Monsieur Binet has a reputable wine cellar. The impecunious are made equally comfortable at the Hostellerie Pascal, where the *patron* speaks Arabic.

The pleasures of Cassis are perhaps less strenuous. Certainly one hires a boat and drifts along the coast to the beautiful *calanques*, as lovely as anything on the Riviera, of Port Miou, Margiou and Sormiou. The local white wine is soporific enough, and in the Bar Simoun of Cassis Thérèse cooks Algerian *couscous* several days a week. In and around Marseilles Africa is never far away.

THE DORDOGNE

by RICHARD CHURCH

THERE ARE certain parts of Europe which I would find it difficult to write about in a cool, topographical way. That is because I have learned to know them, and their characters (for places and districts have characters, just as persons do), and cannot revisit them imaginatively without putting myself into a fervour. It is impossible, in such moods, to remember a mass of details and to catalogue them. I doubt if anybody would require that precision. If they do, it can be found in innumerable guide books and local histories. But when I think of past wanderings in Tuscany, Umbria, the Schwarzwald, the Bernese Oberland, the Roussillon and the Dordogne, my recollections begin to fuse under the heat of the rekindled magic, and all I can offer is an incandescent mass ; a poor substitute for the intimate joys composing it.

So in writing of the Dordogne, I cannot construct a tour, river by river, valley by valley, town by town. The district is a large one, the third largest department in the Napoleonically reconstituted France. Formerly, it was part of the province of Guyon, so closely associated with England's kings and our freebooter history. Survivals of that association may be found everywhere in the Dordogne, as indeed all up the western seaboard of France. To this day, for example, on the island of Oleron, the peasant women wear a kind of deep-edged sunbonnet called a 'Kiss-not.' One spring day I cycled into a tiny village called Rignac (or was it Thégra ?), conspicuous by having its manor house sited right in the middle of the community, at one corner of the Square. But the château was uninhabited, its windows blind, the portals gaping, while one half of the building was roofless. The mischief looked so recent that I approached an old man sitting against a wall in the sun and dust and asked him if the Germans were responsible for this outrage. 'No !' was the laconic reply, 'the English.' I protested, saying that we were never here during the war. That led to further laconics, in the course of which I learned that the old man was referring to the depredations of the Black Prince, which the native was still unwilling to forget.

That incident took place in the less frequented part of the Dordogne, known as the Lot, or the Haut-Quercy. There is no considerably large town in this upland plateau, for even the market town of Gramat lies half-asleep on its aerated rock-bed. This is getting southward in the district, toward Cahors, and coming from Paris the explorer has already left behind the great Y-shaped valleys formed by the conjunction of the two principal rivers, the Dordogne itself and its dreaming tributary, the Vézère. I should cite Cahors as the southern post of this strange, haunted country, with Aurillac and Rodez to the east, Bergerac and Perigeux (the capital of the Dordogne) to the west, and Tulle, or, at a stretch, Limoges, to the north.

Within this vague confine lies the limestone land, a vast ledge separating the Massif Central from the estuarial plain where the vineyards of Bordeaux are threaded on the conjunction of rivers that flow into the Gironde, every mile adding a gradual touch of salinity to the fabulous vintages. The character of this ledge-like countryside is difficult to describe because it is so elusive, almost secretive. Part of it, indeed, lies underground, for the district is like an ossified sponge, blown up and aerated with caves, thousands of them. That is why North European man, at the time of the last Glacial Age, congregated here to seek shelter from the talons of the encroaching glaciers from the Pole. It may explain, too, why the best book written about the Dordogne is by an archaeologist, Mr Glyn Daniel, from whose *Lascaux and Carnac* I quote a paragraph that is informative and also evocative.

'The valley of the Dordogne is full of contrast to the Morbihan coast, and when I write this I am thinking mainly of the Middle Dordogne and its tributary, the Vézère—the area of the prehistoric caves. Here are deep wide valleys with lush water-meadows, the rivers edged with Lombardy poplars. The valleys are cut in limestone which produced the rock-shelters and caves for Upper Paleolithic man's homes and temples : above them are uneven limestone plateaux. The valleys of the Dordogne and Vézère are quiet and beautiful ; the rivers twist and turn along their mature, tree-shaded courses from the Massif Central of France to the sea at Bordeaux ; small châteaux cling, apparently precariously, to the plateau edge, and on the plateau sheep wander. My most vivid memories of the Dordogne countryside are of walks in the still, summer sunshine along the gravelled, yellow, side roads on the plateaux cutting through the woods of chestnut, or of sitting underneath a road-bridge over the river and watching poplars mirrored in the cold, fast, clear water.'

To that vivid picture, I would add something of the half desolate open stretches of the plateaux, called *causses*, a kind of common land traversed only by footpaths or rough horse-rides winding round obtrusions of rock, and flanked by rock plants which in spring offer both perfume and music to the wanderer. For the bushes, of gorse ; and the *planta genesta* which gave a name to a dynasty of English kings ; the hawthorn gnarled and deformed by situation and age ; guelder and rock rose ; elder and occasional wild cherry and crab, are all crowded during their perfume time with nightingales, whose full-throated hour lasts day and night, a symphony of ocarinas and oboes that almost bursts the human ear-drum.

The nature of the soil, sparse and grey, over this upland, has an exhilarating effect upon the spirits of the travellers. It is all so aerated, so giddily light, and at the same time so clean and fragrant. It is as though the green Cotswold landscape had been sent to the bleacher, and put back robbed of half its luxury, and stretched out so wide that its pores had opened, coarsening its texture, and here and there splitting the fabric with long inland fissures of broken cliff, where villages and colonies of swifts and martins clustered, the human and the bird life clinging perilously to the naked scars.

This may be seen at Rocamadour, the town where 'Childe Rolande to the Dark Tower came,' and laid his sword on the altar of the Virgin in the shrine at the top of the steep cliff on which the village hangs. Long before this knight of Charlemagne, during the retreat from the Pyrénées, dedicated himself to religion instead of to war, there came from the East that early devote, Zacchœus, who climbed the sycamore tree in order to see Jesus who was hidden in the crowd of wonder-seekers. The publican, after the death of his wife, Veronique, journeyed westward, preaching the gospel. When a skeleton was discovered in 1166 under a rock in the river Alzou, which makes an elbow bend before the resistance of the cliff at this point, the religious folk accepted as certainty that this must be the relic of the man who had seen the Christ. The place became a centre of pilgrimage, and is so to this day, the process being to climb the hundreds of stone steps *on one's knees*, from the bottom of the village, visiting the six chapels at ascending stages. The figure of the Virgin is of wood, inlaid with silver. It is a primitive carving of the twelfth century, still bearing a Byzantine cast, so far as it can be seen beneath its coating of smoke-grime from centuries of offerings from candle and incense.

If one approaches Rocamadour from the south, through Gramat, it will be necessary to pass the Château de Roumégouse, which stands on the high plateau above the town, in a small park with terraces that give a view of some fifty miles north-westward toward the wine-country, over fold upon fold of hills. The Château is now open to guests, and is run by a couple who retired there after living in London for thirty years. The food they offer is superb ; a cuisine based on the dishes of the Dordogne, which includes the *omelettes aux truffes,* and *escargots.* Though the vineyards of the Dordogne were almost wholly destroyed by the phylloxera, some local wine may still be drunk, as a promise of the recovery of the wines of the district. At the Château I sampled this survival, and found it acceptable, a cousin both to St. Emilion wines and those of the Rhône.

From north to south of what I persist in calling The Province (since the medieval habit both of thought and behaviour still holds there), the gourmet will find satisfaction, especially if he be one who cannot take the rich dishes of Alsace, to which those of the Dordogne may be compared. I recall, too, that at the Château I drank, after dinner, a dry, sparkling Barsac at less than half the price of champagne.

Over the next hill from Roumégouse there is a circular flaw, hundreds of feet deep, and a hundred yards in diameter. Across the bottom of it, which may be reached by a lift, there flows the river, from deep to deep, through caverns of multi-coloured rock, whose vast bastions flow down from roof to floor and water-level, seemingly alive by reason of the trickle of water over their surfaces, that gleam with flesh-tints, bruised and tormented, above their own reflections in the silent stream. For several miles this course can be followed in a punt, culminating in a wide underground lake where all is silent, except for the sullen drip, at minute intervals, from the groins invisible above.

That is but one of the natural wonders of the Dordogne, which abounds in such dramatic gestures and contortions, the last agonies of some volcanic upheaval arrested millions of aeons ago. The débris of that period, loose rocks, miles of ravines and inland cliffs, bastions and crags, is now softened by climate and vegetation, the long caress of air and the drapery of the flora of the *Causse.* Not only the Ancient of the Rocks but Ancient Man as well have left a signature upon this countryside. And the latter affirmation has drawn more tourists than has the former.

The cave paintings and etchings of Les Eyzies and Lascaux have been reproduced in books and written about by art critics and archaeologists. But their awe-striking mystery remains with them in the caves, where they have to be seen before they can be fully appreciated. In their own place, where they have waited for twenty thousand years for an appreciative public, they baffle the conscious mind, almost cheating the imagination, just as a vast landscape, or Handel's *Messiah*, or Donatello's *David*, will tease the aspirant with out-of-bound promises and half-revelations. One thing I noticed at Lascaux, not commented on in the books, was the thumb-nail scratchings of files of little figures. Were they records of some kind, and was the cave a bank as well as a temple ? That would give this early religion a modern touch.

As I predicted early in this essay, I have been unable to do the rounds of the Dordogne. I could continue, town by town, scar by scar, pointing out the individual characteristics. I would like to stop at Souillac, for example, and visit the round church of the Knights Templar, and the lovely villas along the banks of the River Dordogne. Here the poet Nancy Cunard lives for part of the year, adding to her scholarship of the literature of the South, which another English poet, Richard Aldington, knows so well. And there is Carennac, where the family of Fenelon settled in the sixteenth century.

The castles, the grottoes, the sanctuaries, the fantasies of nature, are to be found in profusion. None of them, however, is so overwhelming as the one I have mentioned, the Gouffre de Padirac, near the Château de Roumégouse, above Rocamadour. Even the wonders of Les Eyzies and Lascaux become almost comprehensible in comparison with that dreadful silence of waters flowing 'through caverns measureless to man' out through that underground lake, where I once looked at the very presence of Nothingness, my mind as stricken into awe and fear as that of the artists of twenty thousand years ago, when they painted their propitiations on the walls of the caverns, hoping to ease the torment of the Mystery.

LA BELLE ISEULT

by PHILIP HENDERSON

O N E O F the most closely kept secrets of the Victorian age is the story of the long love affair between Rossetti and Jane, the wife of William Morris. Watts-Dunton declared that he would go to the grave without disclosing what he knew, and Rossetti himself showed evident nervousness lest the all-too-revealing sonnets in *The House of Life* should be interpreted biographically. He did his best to put posterity off the scent. But posterity is always curious, and its curiosity in this case has not been lessened by the knowledge that the letters between Rossetti and Jane Morris, deposited in the British Museum in 1939, may not, under the terms of May Morris's bequest, be consulted until 1989. What need, one may well wonder, when everyone concerned has been dead for so long, for all this mystery ?

Turning for guidance to that Bible of the later Pre-Raphaelites, the *Morte d'Arthur*, one finds a parallel situation. King Arthur condoned, or ignored, as long as he could the love between Lancelot and Guenevere, not only because it was in the tradition of courtly love, but because his own love for Lancelot and his other knights was far stronger than the lukewarm relationship with his wife. When Lancelot is actually discovered in the queen's chamber—'And whether they were abed or at other manner of disports, me list not hereof make no mention,' says Malory slyly—and she is condemned to be burnt for treason, after remarking in an off-hand manner—'She shall have the law' and promising Lancelot a shameful death if he can be taken,

Arthur's final comment on the whole affair is : 'and much more 1 am sorrier for my good knights' loss than for the loss of my fair queen ; for queens I might have enow, but such a fellowship of goodly knights shall never be together in no company' (Book XX, ch. IX).

It was as a fellowship of goodly knights that Morris, Rossetti, Burne-Jones, Philip Webb and company saw themselves at Oxford in 1857. Morris even had a suit of mail made by a local smith and used to dine in it. They were banded together in 'a crusade and holy warfare against the age,' vowed to seek the grail of beauty amidst the encircling gloom of Victorian industrialism. Thus it is hardly an exaggeration to suppose that Morris's love for his friends and fellow crusaders meant more to him, by and large, that his frustrating relationship with his picturesque but dumb wife. Indeed, he seems to have had a foreknowledge of the tragic emotional pattern of his life, and to some extent it was self-willed. As a poet, he began by writing his *Defence of Guenevere*. In this he differed from Tennyson, the upholder of Victorian morality, who makes Guenevere the snake in the grass of his *Idylls of the King*, conveniently forgetting that in Malory the ruin of the realm of Logres comes about just as much through 'the stainless Arthur's' incestuous passion for his own sister, Morgana le Fay, by whom he has Mordred. Again when Morris came to decorate the walls of the Oxford Union, he chose as the subject of his particular fresco 'How Sir Palomides loved La Belle Iseult with exceeding great love out of measure, and how she loved not him again, but rather Sir Tristram.' He was not to know at that time, of course, that the man whom he admired above all others, Rossetti, was to be cast for the rôle of Tristram in his own domestic drama !

It was Rossetti who had first spotted the 'stunner' Jane Burden at the theatre at Oxford one summer evening in 1857, and had at once got into conversation with her. Thus Jane, the daughter of a livery stable keeper in Hollywell, metamorphosed into La Belle Iseult, became the centre of the group of young enthusiasts who were working at the Union and drawing and painting medieval subjects for all they were worth. In fact, she took the place once occupied by Lizzie Siddal (Guggums) among the original Pre-Raphaelite Brotherhood. Both girls came from humble origins and Janey must have felt completely at sea in this company of ardent medievalists, though she probably enjoyed the chaff and horseplay of which Morris ('good old Top'), was always the butt. So ready was Morris to blame himself when anything went wrong that he was known to deal his own head resounding blows with his powerful fists. But when he was really angry, he threw himself to the ground and gnawed the carpet in a genuine Plantagenet rage. Such habits must have made him at once endearing and somewhat trying to live with.

From the first Janey was required to pose, while Morris and Rossetti drew and painted her as Guenevere and Iseult. Not unnaturally the habit grew, and she went on posing for the rest of her life, until she became the most stunning production of Morris and Co., a living exhibit of medieval loveliness. The strain must have been considerable—especially as now both Morris and Rossetti appear to have fallen for her. Morris is said to have passed her a note, as he worked, saying 'I cannot paint you, but I love you,' and in one of his early poems he has left an equally careful portrait of her in words :

> My lady seems of ivory
> Forehead, straight nose, and cheeks that be
> Hollow'd a little mournfully.
> *Beata mea Domina !*
>
> Her forehead, overshadow'd much
> By bows of hair, has a wave such
> As God was good to make for me.
> *Beata mea Domina !*
>
> Not greatly long my lady's hair,
> Nor yet with yellow colour fair,
> But thick and crispéd wonderfully :
> *Beata mea Domina ! . . .*
>
> Her great eyes, standing far apart,
> Draw up some memory from her heart,
> And gaze out very mournfully.
> *Beata mea Domina !*
>
> So beautiful and kind they are
> But most times looking out afar,
> Waiting for something, not for me . . .
>
> Her full lips being made to kiss,
> Curl'd up and pensive each one is,
> This makes me faint to stand and see :
> *Beata mea Domina.*

William Morris in the 'Earthly Paradise' period
Attributed to Charles Fairfax Murray.   National Portrait Gallery

It seems that at this time to stand and stare was about all he could do. His idea of courtship, we are told, was to read to his lady for hours in a very loud voice from *Barnaby Rudge*, fidgetting about and nervously playing with his watch-chain the while. Naturally gruff and abrupt, with women Morris was still more shy and awkward. Is it surprising if Jane Burden preferred the fascinating Mr Rossetti with his Italian blood? But Mr Morris was rich, and doubtless the livery stable keeper told his daughter that she would be a fool to miss such a chance. So she married him in April, 1859, at the age of twenty, and was at once whisked off on a tour of France, Belgium and the Rhineland, to look at pictures, churches and castles.

Next year, after an engagement of nine years, during which his original passion had had plenty of time to cool, Rossetti at last married Guggums—'out of a mistaken sense of loyalty and fear of giving pain,' as Hall Caine reports him as confessing during a dreary night-journey down from Cumberland. By this time, of course, Guggums was already a confirmed invalid and the marriage had, as Rossetti said in a letter to his mother at this time, 'been deferred almost beyond possibility.' On their honeymoon he did his nightmare study 'How They Met Themselves.' Less than two years later Guggums was dead from an overdose of laudanum, and Rossetti was left with his load of guilt and remorse. He had fallen in love with Jane Burden at Oxford, he told Hall Caine, and from this had come all the subsequent bitterness of his life. After the 'Beata Beatrix' of 1863, in which he painted Lizzie 'in a trance of death,' Janey took her place as the Beatrice of his adoration. He was to paint her dead, too, in 'Dante's Dream,' but never was so glamorous a corpse. In all these paintings of Jane Morris, there is the same brooding, frustrated sexuality. When he painted her as Pandora, dressed in a red Venetian gown and carrying a casket from which arose fumes of spirit forms, he described these in an accompanying sonnet as 'powers of impassioned hours prohibited.' In 'La Pia' she is seen as the wife of Nello della Pietra (the incident is from the fifth canto of the *Purgatorio*), shut up by a cruel husband to die in a fortress built in the poisonous Maremma marshes in revenge for her love of Dante. 'With one hand she fingers the wedding-ring that has brought her so much sorrow,' comments Marillier ! In the guise of Proserpine, the imprisoned bride of Pluto, she is seen again 'brooding in the cold light of the subterranean palace of her winter exile,' as Evelyn Waugh writes in his early study of Rossetti, 'Mrs Morris as she filled his dream . . .' Yet Morris seems to have loved this picture and hung it in the dining-room at Queen Square, Bloomsbury, where Henry James saw it in 1869. It was, says James, an extremely good likeness, 'yet so strange and unreal that if you hadn't seen her you'd pronounce it a distempered vision. . .' And he goes on to describe 'a tall lean woman in a long dress of some dead purple stuff, guiltless of hoops . . . with a mass of crisp black hair heaped into great wavy projections on each side of her temples, a thin pale face, a pair of strange, sad, deep, dark Swinburnian eyes, with great thick black oblique brows, joined in the middle and tucking themselves away under her hair, a mouth like the "Oriana" in our illustrated Tennyson, a long neck, without any collar, and in lieu thereof some dozen strings of outlandish beads.' After dinner, while Morris read out some unpublished parts of *The Earthly Paradise*, Jane lay on the sofa, a handkerchief over her face, with toothache. Morris, James notes, 'is extremely pleasant and quite different from his wife. He impressed me most agreeably. He is short, burly, corpulent . . . He has a very loud voice and a nervous restless manner and a perfectly unaffected and business-like address. His talk, indeed, is wonderfully to the point and remarkable for clear good sense . . . He's an extraordinary example, in short, of a delicate sensitive genius and taste, saved by a perfectly healthy body and temper.' In all this neurotic, over-charged atmosphere there is something very refreshing in Morris's reply to a host who ventured to ask him one morning at breakfast whether he had slept well. 'Of course I did,' said Morris, 'what do you think I went to bed for ?'

Yet, from the first, Morris seems to have been haunted in his poetry by the figure of the despised and rejected lover, complemented by the tormenting image of the brilliant and successful rival. One need not look too far afield for the originals of these two images, especially as about this time Morris wrote an uncompleted novel about two brothers who had fallen in love with the same woman. He did not finish the novel, he says, because he 'could not see how it would work out !' In short, the years during which he was working at *The Earthly Paradise*—that is, the mid-sixties—seem to have been very far from an earthly paradise for *him*. He had by now evidently woken up to the unpleasant fact that his wife, who had already declined into that state of invalidism in which she was to remain on and off for the rest of her life, did not return his love. In the charming verses on the months that introduce the various books of *The Earthly Paradise*, he has written, says Mackail, 'an autobiography so delicate and so outspoken that it must be left to speak for itself.' Thus in the verses on September he sees himself as a new-wakened man

> . . . who tries
> To dream again the dream that made him glad
> When in his arms his loving love he had.

The lines on January are more revealing still of the strange baffled relationship between Morris and his Belle Iseult.

From this dull rainy undersky and low,
The murky ending of a leaden day,
That never knew the sun, this half-thawed snow,
These tossing black boughs faint against the gray
Of gathering night, thou turnest, dear, away
Silent, but with thy scarce-seen kindly smile
Sent through the dusk my longing to beguile.

There, the lights gleam, and all is dark without,
And in the sudden change our eyes meet dazed—
O look, love, look again ! the veil of doubt
Just for one flash, past counting, then was raised !
O eyes of heaven, as clear thy sweet soul blazed
On mine a moment ! O come back again
Strange rest and dear amid the long dull pain.

It is not often that Morris allowed his stifled emotions to come to the surface in this way. His ideal was a cheerful manliness and his bluff mask deceived most people. In reality he was a complex, highly nervous character, full of hidden conflicts and baffled emotion.

Mackail confesses his difficulty in dealing with this period in his classic biography, for he was writing during the lifetime of the rest of the Morris family. 'Of course my difficulties over the work itself were great,' he tells Mrs. Coronio, one of Morris's more intimate women friends, in a letter of May, 1899, 'especially in the constant need for what is called "tact," which is a quality unpleasantly near untruthfulness often : and especially I feel that my account of all those stormy years of the *Earthly Paradise* time and the time following it must be excessively flat owing to the amount of tact that had to be exercised right and left.'

Outwardly, of course, the life at Red House presented a spectacle of domestic felicity. Jenny and May had been born in the early sixties, Rossetti was still the valued friend and master and collaborated with the others in making the house at Bexley Heath into a Palace of Art. The Burne-Joneses, Swinburne and Madox Brown came for the week-ends, and good cheer flowed in abundance. Undergraduate horse-play and practical jokes went on as before, and 'good old Top' was always the butt. They would put a tuck in the back of his waist-coat, so that he would think that he had grown several inches fatter during the night ; or they would send him to Coventry at his own dinner-table and talk about him as though he were not there, while everyone became helpless with laughter. But perhaps the fun was getting just a shade hysterical. At any rate, it was not to last much longer. In 1865 Morris went down with a severe attack of rheumatic fever. On his recovery, he gave up Red House and moved to Queen Square, where he lived above his work-rooms.

In the summer of 1871 he took Kelmscott Manor, Lechlade, jointly with Rossetti, and at once set off to explore the saga sites of Iceland. Was it also to get away from an intolerable situation ? For in spite of the atmosphere of secrecy and suspense in the sonnets that Rossetti was writing at this time, and their often rather abstruse symbolism, many are frank and straightforward, with a frankness rare in Victorian poetry. 'Silent Noon,' for instance, is clearly a description of Janey and Gabriel lying side by side in the fields at Kelmscott.

> Your hands lie open in the long fresh grass,—
>   The finger-points look through like rosy blooms ;
>   Your eyes smile peace. The pasture gleams and glooms
> 'Neath billowing skies that scatter and amass.
> All round our nest, far as the eye can pass,
>   Are golden kingcup-fields with silver edge
>   Where the cow-parsley skirts the hawthorn hedge.
> 'Tis visible silence, still as the hour-glass.
>
> Deep in the sun-searched growths the dragon-fly
> Hangs like a blue thread loosened from the sky :—
>   So this wing'd hour is dropt to us from above.
> Oh ! clasp we to our hearts, for deathless dower,
> This close-companioned inarticulate hour
>   When twofold silence was the song of love.

'Supreme Surrender' had already appeared in the 1870 volume (which also included 'Nuptial Sleep,' later suppressed) and must therefore have been written in the late sixties.

> The bliss so long afar, at length so nigh,
>   Rests here attained. Methinks proud Love must weep
>   When Fate's control doth from his harvest reap
> The sacred hour for which the years did sigh.
>
> First touched, the hand now warm around my neck
>   Taught memory long to mock desire : and lo !
>   Across my breast the abandoned hair doth flow,
> Where one shorn tress long stirred the longing ache :
> And next the heart that trembled for its sake
>   Lies the queen-heart in sovereign overthrow.

If this, with its faded 'poetic' vocabulary and hackneyed tropes, means anything at all, it means that Rossetti had been in love with Jane for years and that now he possessed her. 'At Last' and 'First Fire' were excluded from the *Collected Poems* of 1886 (edited by W. M. Rossetti) as being too revealing. 'First Fire' is quoted by Professor Oswald Doughty in his fascinating study *A Victorian Romantic : Dante Gabriel Rossetti*, the first book thoroughly to explore this whole problem.

> This hour be her sweet body all my song.
> > Now the same heart-beat blends her gaze with mine,
> > One parted fire, love's silent countersign.
> Her arms lie open, throbbing with their throng
> Of confluent pulses, bare and fair and strong ;
> > And her deep-freighted lips expect me now,
> > Amid the clustering hair that shrines her brow
> Five kisses broad, her neck ten kisses long.

Evidently Rossetti did not exaggerate the length of Janey's neck in his paintings. But there was nothing fragile about her, like Guggums, although she always appears in his pictures with the requisite Pre-Raphaelite droop. The trouble was, perhaps, that far greater demands were made upon her than her essentially commonplace nature was capable of responding to.

Fearing that his readers would see them for what they really were, Rossetti pretended that most of the sonnets in *The House of Life* had been written at a much earlier date and were addressed to his dead wife. From their context, however, it appears that many of them were written between 1868 and 1877. Twenty-seven of them belong to the year 1871 alone, and were evidently written at Kelmscott. But it is in the 'Willow-wood' series that Rossetti first acknowledged to himself his long-suppressed love for Mrs Morris, as he gazes down at her face reflected in the water of a well.

> Then the dark ripples spread to waving hair,
> And as I stooped, her own lips rising there
> > Bubbled with brimming kisses at my mouth.

Though he may have unconsciously recalled Keats's beaker of the warm south with its beaded bubbles winking at the brim, there is something unpleasant about the image of bubbling kisses. It is the kind of vulgarity we often encounter in Rossetti's work, never in Morris's.

Jane Morris: a hitherto unpublished photograph

Morris must have had a pretty shrewd idea of what was going on at Kelmscott during his absence in Iceland. But he pretended not to know. 'I know now clearer perhaps than then, what a blessing last year's journey was to me,' he writes to Mrs Coronio in November, 1872, 'what horrors it saved me from.' Earlier in the same letter—the most revealing letter of his to survive—he remarks : 'When I said there was no cause for my feeling low, I meant that my friends had not changed at all towards me in any way and that there had been no quarrelling : and indeed I am afraid it comes from some cowardice and unmanliness in me. One thing wanting ought not to go for so much : nor indeed does it spoil my enjoyment of life always, as I have often told you : to have real friends and some sort of an aim in life is so much, that I ought to think myself lucky : and often in my better moods I wonder what it is in me that throws me into such rage and despair at other times. I suspect, do you know, that some such moods would have come upon me at times even without this failure of mine . . . Oh how I long to keep the world from narrowing on me, and to look at things bigly and kindly !'

It is clear that Morris blamed himself, and no one else, for the failure of his marriage. It was he who had invested Jane Burden with the qualities of La Belle Iseult, and he could hardly blame her now if she turned out after all to be only the livery stable keeper's daughter, who preferred tea-parties and gossip to Chaucer and Froissart, though she *was* very skilful with her needle.

Nevertheless, he was beginning to lose patience with Rossetti. 'Rossetti has set himself down at Kelmscott as if he never meant to go away,' he complains to Mrs Coronio, 'and not only does that keep me from that harbour of refuge (because it is a farce our meeting when we can help it) but also he has all sorts of ways so unsympathetic to the sweet simple old place, that I feel his presence there as a kind of slur on it : this is very unreasonable though when one thinks why one took the place . . .' According to Victorian morality—indeed, according to still accepted standards—he should no doubt have taken his old friend by the scruff of the neck and flung him out. But his attitude to the whole thing is clear from the beautiful and neglected poem on the Paris Commune, 'The Pilgrims of Hope,' written more than ten years later, where the hero discovers that his best friend has secretly become his wife's lover and generously forgives them both. Compassion and sorrow are the dominant feelings here, neither self-pity nor anger. Thus, while at Kelmscott, Rossetti's sonnets temporarily glowed with fulfilled love, after *The Defence of Guenevere* Morris's poetry becomes anaemic with stifled emotion. On his return from Iceland in 1872 he was driven to create for himself a compensatory world within a world, where Pharamond, in *Love is Enough*, leaves his kingdom and wanders through the world in search of an ideal love—or in other words, a dream mistress. There is a moment of disagreeable reality, however, when the personified figure of Love enters, for she comes to Pharamond with bloody hands and a bitter drink, and he cries : 'A dream and a lie, and my death !'

Rossetti left Kelmscott for good in 1874, returning to the great, gloomy house in Cheyne Walk, to Fanny and his domestic zoo— though by this time the wombat and the kangaroo had escaped to neighbouring gardens. He bought an Indian bull instead, because it had eyes that reminded him of Janey Morris. Resorting to more and more enormous doses of chloral in order to sleep at all, he became increasingly the victim of his neurosis, his mind sucked down into a whirlpool of obsessive emotions.

Then again, after Robert Buchanan's attack on his poetry, persecution mania grew upon him to such an extent that he used to hear voices insulting him at night. One day, while walking beside the river at Kelmscott, he had turned upon some fishermen, whom he imagined to have insulted him, and overwhelmed them with abuse. After that there was nothing for it but to leave the neighbourhood. Eight years of life now remained to Rossetti. During them he worked hard, both at poetry and painting, doing replicas of his old pictures, which he sold at high prices to northern manufacturers. His money he kept in coffers, dispensing handfuls of gold to his more needy friends, like some Renaissance prince. Morris he never saw again, but Janey visited him from time to time and, in the rather horrific 'Day Dream,' he painted her sitting in the fork of the sycamore in his garden. It is said to have been his favourite picture of her, though the face he put in from a study made years earlier.

It was a weary, bitter, frustrated life. His only comfort was the overblown Fanny Cornforth, soon to become the landlady of the 'Rose and Crown' in Jermyn Street. 'Good elephant,' he wrote to her pathetically, 'do come down. Old Rhinoceros is unhappy.' How well this pet name fitted him can be seen by turning to Max Beerbohm's 'Rossetti and his Circle.'

After his departure from Kelmscott, Janey collapsed again and had to be sent to the Italian Riviera to recuperate, with May and Jenny, who was by this time subject to epileptic fits. Rossetti's death in 1882 precipitated another crisis. Perhaps it was only then that the whole story came out. As Morris remarked with his usual downrightness, to James Mavor : 'Sometimes Rossetti was an angel, and sometimes he was a damned scoundrel.'

Meanwhile Morris worked harder than ever, producing hundreds of designs for wallpapers, chintzes, carpets and curtains—designs which, it must be admitted, do not always escape the stuffiness of that over-upholstered age. 'I have spent, I know, a vast amount of time designing furniture and wallpapers, carpets and curtains,' he once confessed to Cunninghame Graham, 'but after all I am inclined to think that that sort of thing is mostly rubbish, and I would prefer for myself to live with the plainest white-washed walls and wooden chairs and tables.' What a confession after a lifetime spent covering every blank space he

Opposite : '*The Day Dream*
by Dante Gabriel Rossetti
Victoria and Albert Museum

could find (even the borders of books) with obsessive patterns ! But he was now, as he told people, 'a man of the north,' and saw himself as Sigurd the Volsung. As the orders poured in upon him at Merton Abbey, his rages grew ever more terrible. He kicked panels out of doors, threw his food out of the window (when it was badly cooked), ground his teeth as he stood waiting for trains at Earls Court, and swore like a trooper. But much of this rage and frustration he now canalized into revolutionary politics, and since his wife had proved such a broken reed he put his frustrated love for her into what he called 'the religion of socialism'—addressing crowds of workers from slag-heaps in the north and, a venerable white-haired figure, running three-legged races with the comrades during outings at Petersham. On a voyage to Norway in the last year of his life, he was terrified by the coils of rope lying on deck, for they appeared to his disordered mind like a great serpent preparing to crush the life out of him. He was, Mrs A. M. W. Stirling tells us, haunted by these coils till he died. When he died at the age of sixty-two in 1896, the doctor said that his death was simply due to being William Morris and doing the work of ten men.

After her husband's death La Belle Iseult aged beautifully in her moated grange at Kelmscott. The only thing she did not do was to get into a barge, like that equally hysterical 'lily maid' of Astolat, and float down the river singing till she died. Instead, she lived on, a semi-invalid in mourning for her life, until 1914, the tragic guardian of her epileptic daughter, Jenny. 'I fancy,' writes Graham Robertson, who met her in her later years, 'that her mystic beauty must sometimes have weighed rather heavily upon her. Her mind was not formed upon the same tragic lines as her face ; she was very simple and could have enjoyed simple pleasures with simple people, but such delights were not for her . . . She was a Ladye in a Bower, an ensorcelled Princess, a Blessed Damozel, while I feel sure she would have preferred to be a "bright chatty little woman" in request for small theatre parties and afternoons up the river. Brightness might equally have been expected from Deirdre of the Sorrows, chattiness from the Sphinx . . . I can well understand that her type was too grand, too sombre to appeal to every age.' Yes, Janey was certainly a stunner. But was she, after all, ever much more than a mournful Pre-Raphaelite pin-up, created out of the fervid romantic imaginations of Morris and Rossetti to torment them both ?

'La Belle Iseult,' by William Morris. Tate Gallery

THE CULINARY CAMPAIGNS OF
ALEXIS SOYER
by H. A. HAMMELMANN

IT WAS in the spring of 1851, just as the Great Exhibition
of all Nations in Hyde Park opened its gates, that Thackeray,
writing in *Punch* under the pseudonym of M. Goubemouche, a
visitor from France, uncovered what he called 'the French conspira-
tion.' What could the terrible danger be that threatened this island
from across the Channel ? One of the periodic alarms, perhaps, lest
the new Napoleon might venture where even his uncle had failed ?
No ; it was the 'Parisian civilization' that had 'invaded and conquered
the white cliffs at which Napoleon pointed in vain his eyeglass and his
flotillas.' Not by sabres and bayonets, but by her intelligence, her
genius, France conspired to vanquish ; and the great pacific conqueror
turned out to be a—cook.

Sallying forth one morning to visit the great Crystal Palace,
Thackeray declared, he had wandered, by mistake, into a rival venture
no less marvellous : the 'Gastronomic Symposium of all Nations' next-
door, designed not to demonstrate the astounding achievements of
industry, but the miracles the kitchen spoon could work even in
England when wielded by so competent and confident a master as
Alexis Soyer.

To revolutionize cookery in England, and to civilize what might a ppear to any Frenchman as the barbarous culinary customs of the natives—that indeed was the ambition of the ingenious little cook from Meaux. Scope for such a reformer there certainly was. In wealthy Victorian England more money was spent on food per head of population than anywhere else in the world ; and for the quality of their meat and other ingredients Englishmen were described as 'the best fed in Europe.' Meals, on the other hand, were heavy, monotonous and dreary, the preparation of the food below criticism and wastage stupendous. 'The British people have done mighty things in the course of their history,' wrote an exasperated journalist of the time ; 'they have created a vast Empire and established a Greater Britain at the antipodes ; they have practically invented the steam-engine and railroads, actually invented penny postage, but they have never, as a nation, been able to make omelettes properly, and never will do so.'

Soyer, though only twenty-one when he arrived in this country, straight from M. de Polignac's kitchens at the Quai d'Orsay, determined to alter all that. His début in London, as *chef de cuisine* at the Reform Club, the fashionable meeting place of the Liberals in their heyday, was auspicious enough. His dinners fascinated and enraptured members ; his banquets became the talk of the town. Even such stately organs as *The Times* and *The Athenaeum* reported with evident relish on the great cook's repasts.

To read one of the thousands of magnificent menus on which Soyer lavished the skill and devotion of a true artist, and to recall the names, composed in 'the florid Gothick style,' which he bestowed upon his creations, is to be lifted into regions where the palate, in our more austere days, can hardly hope to follow. There was for example his 'Celestial and Terrestrial Cream of Great Britain,' the ingredients of which celebrated the charms of fashionable Englishwomen of the day and blended, as *Punch* had it, poetry, party and politics with considerable skill. If the '*desert floréal à la Watteau*' was a tribute to France, another newspaper saw in his 'Round of Beef *à la* Magna Charta,' served at a dinner in honour of Scribe and Halevy, 'the very philosophy of English history put into the compass of one dish ; plain, solid, somewhat heavy . . . satisfactory.' Sometimes, a predilection for practical jokes carried Soyer beyond what was strictly necessary from the gastronomic point of view, as in an elegant dish described, in honour of the famous danseuse, as '*La Croustade Sylphe à la Cerito*.' When the lid was removed, out flew, to the astonishment of all present, a beautiful white pigeon. It was only after opening a false bottom that diners found their satisfaction in filets of grouse and some artificial *cotelettes* 'sweetly resting on a *crème au pêches.*'

Such gastronomic extravaganzas were of course only for the happy few, but Soyer, the chef, was not content to cater, in his 'sanctorum' at the Reform Club, for aristocratic Society alone ; he dreamt of reforming the cookery of the whole country. Since he wielded the pen with the same agility and originality as the saucepan, cookery books for every need soon made their appearance. There was a *Gastronomic Regenerator* reserved for gourmets ; a collection of recipes for the middle classes, the *Modern Housewife*, and yet another, most urgently required of all, to tell the poor how to make the most of their food. The *Modern Housewife*, still a standard cookery book, lively, full of good sense and admirable advice as it is, sold ten thousand copies in the first fortnight and made the author financially independent ; but the best proof of its success was perhaps the appearance of a press advertisement in which 'a rich bachelor of untold property' offered to marry the original of Soyer's housewife on one condition only : that he should have an opportunity, before accepting the young lady's hand, of testing its lightness in making pies and puddings.

It was his *Shilling Cookery for the People*, however, which finally and firmly established Soyer's fame. In purchasing this best-seller, which topped the quarter-million mark, a shilling was certainly well laid out, for here, almost for the first time, nutritious, wholesome, quickly and economically prepared food was offered in recipes fitted to the most modest purses. If that were not enough, Soyer invented a simple 'Magic Stove,' equally serviceable, so it was said, 'in the parlour of the wealthy, the studio of the artist and the attic of the humble,' and, above all, cheap. Practical help like this proved invaluable in the hungry 'forties, not least during the potato famine in Ireland, when the great *chef* himself for a while ran soup-kitchens in Dublin and earned for himself the title of 'Gastronomic Regenerator of Ireland.'

'The only true Minister of the Interior,' 'King Soyer,' 'Emperor of the Kitchen,' such were other titles bestowed by an admiring press and public on the incomparable French cook. Strolling about in an *opéra buffa* costume and a *béret* obliquely angled '*à la zoug-zoug*,' swinging his cane, and ever ready with a pun produced with an inimitable French accent, Soyer (who always had an eye for the picturesque) became a familiar sight in the streets of London. A true showman, he knew the value of publicity and used it to place his reign on ever vaster foundations. Rumour, for instance, had it that he was at the bottom of a petition presented to Parliament in 1845 which prayed for the establishment of a College of Cookery to provide for a hitherto shamefully neglected branch in the education of young ladies. However that may be, it is certainly true that Soyer attempted to enlist, more than once, the support of what he termed 'the other arts' for the spreading of his culinary gospel. Thackeray's literary support was not enough ; the painters, too, were exhorted to employ their genius and their brushes on such useful and interesting subjects as the kitchen and its history, instead of 'continually tracing on innumerable yards of canvas the horrors of war, the plague, the storms and earthquakes.' Historic events which struck Soyer as worthy of commemoration were such touching scenes as Cardinal Mazarin taking, at the Louvre, 'the first cup of chocolate' ; but here for once he was topped, at his own game, by Mr. Punch's proposal of a grand historical painting immortalizing 'the courage of the Great Unknown who swallowed the first oyster.'

The opportunity of putting into practice the whole range of his grandiose ideas came to Alexis Soyer with the great Industrial Exhibition of 1851. For fear of accidental fire in the vast glass structure of the exhibition building, no cooking was to be allowed in the Crystal Palace ; while, for other reasons, presumably no less practical, no alcoholic drinks of any kind were to be served there. Among the stale buns provided in the official refreshment room, the meagre sandwiches, lemonade and, to quote once more from *Punch*, 'an object not very rare in the metropolis, but still in its way curious,—namely a lukewarm ice,' exhausted visitors to the exhibition might have found themselves in a sore plight after their wanderings through endless corridors of the Palace of Industry, had not Soyer come to their rescue. Since proper food and drink was not to be had inside, he decided to set up within a stone's throw a full-fledged restaurant, his Gastronomic Symposium of all Nations, which was to be imposing and astonishing as anything within the great glass-house. To out-do the Crystal Palace was indeed an immense challenge ; Soyer rose to it majestically, even if it must with regret be related that this venture, unlike almost everything else he took in hand, did not at last prove successful.

[157]

Neither expense nor effort were spared to render the Universal Symposium a seat of luscious epicurean pleasures. Five to six thousand guests were to be entertained daily, and even Gore House, Lady Blessington's splendid mansion next to Hyde Park, on the site now occupied by the Albert Hall, looked hardly large enough to accommodate them all. Assisted by George Augustus Sala, a versatile journalist whose power of imagination almost rivalled that of the famous *chef* himself, Soyer transformed the building and its gardens according to conceptions taken straight from the *Arabian Nights*. One apartment, flamed in crimson and yellow, and enlivened by fantastic Chinese dragons and lanterns, was surmounted by a huge golden sun and thus made to represent an Oriental eating house. Lady Blessington's boudoir next door, decorated with stalactites and piled with eternal snow, suggested the North Pole or Kamchatka. A description of these superlative if garish flights of fancy filled about fifty pages of a prospectus : there were, among many other no less striking features, '*La Vestibule de la fille d'Orage*,' '*La Forêt Peruvienne* or the Night of Stars,' a 'Bower of Ariadne' and a 'Transatlantic Passage,' the 'Door of the Dungeon of Mystery,' a 'Lilliputian Kitchen,' and, last not least, the magnificent marble staircase adorned with a '*Macedoine* of all Nations,' at the top of which Soyer was wont to receive his guests. The international 'Fruit Salad' was not, it should be explained, a matter for the palate, but a panoramic fresco painting of Sala's, incorporating every living and dead celebrity imaginable, where Napoleon, Guizot, Dumas and Victor Hugo rubbed shoulders with Wellington, Disraeli and Thackeray himself, who was once seen contemplating his likeness with somewhat mixed feelings.

It was obviously difficult even for the best of *chefs* to cook up to the standard of these incomparable decorations ; yet that was not the cause of Soyer's troubles. At first everybody was eager to inspect the astonishing Symposium ; but once the first curiosity had worn off, few apparently cared to be seen there again. Attendances fell even when dancing and balloon ascents for all comers were added to the attractions ; but expenses kept on rising. Eventually Soyer had to realize that the money extravagantly spent on his great entertainment could never be recovered. When, in addition, he found that neither the neighbours nor the authorities shared his enthusiasm for the noisy establishment, the *Chef* abruptly closed down, finding himself almost down to his last penny.

The failure of this grand and colourful scheme was a sad reverse, but if it sobered Soyer, it did not daunt him. His reforming zeal remained undiminished. The Crimean war, three years later, offered him his chance of true and lasting greatness, and he took it with both hands. Within a few months of the outbreak of fighting in the East grave complaint was heard of the cooking in the Army before Sebastopol —or rather of the want of it. In the strategic counsels of war among the disparate Allies, so historians have said, too many cooks spoilt the broth ; in another, more literal sense, however, there were too few. The men actually engaged in battle, more often than not had to cook their own food. As they crept back from the trenches, cold and weary, there was nothing but wet wood to light a fire, and it might take a man an hour or more to fry his piece of salt meat. As a result, so one war correspondent wrote, 'with the exception of their biscuit, the men have been for weeks entirely living upon uncooked victuals. Through scarcity of fuel and perfect ignorance of cooking, the beef and pork is swallowed usually just as it is served out, and in many cases I have known, even the coffee has been *eaten*, without so much as being roasted.'

When these stories of ignorance and neglect, mismanagement and stupidity in the Crimea became known in London, Soyer—on the spur of the moment—wrote a letter to *The Times* offering to go out at his own expense and devote himself to the reformation of the kitchen at the seat of war. The offer was avidly accepted by a government under heavy pressure from public opinion. Personal inspection in the Crimea and at Scutari soon convinced the cook that the appalling reports received at home had not been exaggerated. In the hospital kitchen, in as far as he could see at all through the blinding wood smoke, he found bad charcoal burners, burnt rice-pudding, unseasoned broth, and hardly any organization at all. Few of the so-called 'cooks'— common soldiers indiscriminately assigned to this fatigue for seven-day spells—had ever cooked before ; hardly one had even the most rudimentary notions of the preparation of food for a large number of men. Their utensils were inadequate or non-existent, their skill nil, and it was not surprising that the men preferred duty in the trenches to working in the cook-houses built of mud to the size of pig-styes.

With his customary zest and tireless energy, Soyer got down to 'setting things to rights.' It was the most important assignment he ever had, and also, as it proved, the most congenial. Soyer, so he said in his own account of the experience, felt 'more proud to work for the soldiers than ever I did in working for the greatest epicures and the first lords of England.' Within two months of his arrival at the front, he 'opened fire' at his new kitchen built of stoves of his own designs, and in the presence of the three Allied Commanders-in-Chief provided an excellent meal for his guests on the spot out of army rations. He set up bakeries and invented a biscuit which kept, and tasted, far better than the 'iron ration' hitherto supplied to the troops. He drew up recipes for meat and vegetables (they were published, at home, in *The Times*), and had them distributed to each unit ; he trained the cooks and instructed them in the essentials of cleanliness. Permanent cookery sergeants were appointed. Soyer saw to everything : he improved the soldier's teapots, economized their fuel, taught them to flavour their rations ; in fact he wielded 'a magical spoon' that, with one motion, transformed what before was 'half-raw or boiled-to-rags mutton, cold potatoes and greasy soup to rations succulent, delicious !' No wonder, then, that with his obliquely angled *béret* he rapidly became 'the soldiers' friend,' a popular and familiar if somewhat eccentric figure in the camp who had gained the affection and gratitude of the whole army, astonishing all, from private to general, by the transformation he had wrought.

The full story of Soyer's part in the war in the East can be read in the last and in many ways the most amusing book he wrote, his *Culinary Campaign in the Crimea* (1857), which nicely mixes glorification of his exploits around the battlefields with sound kitchen sense. 'The literary portions [of this work],' he writes in his Preface, 'the Author has dished up to the best of his ability,' and indeed this final feat of our garrulous genius is nothing if not succulent. Tremendous *raconteur* that he was, the great Chef builds up the account of his 'Campaign' just as, in his heyday at the Reform Club, he used to devise one of his most staggering banquets. Striking or amusing stories from the front and from the kitchen stove follow each other in almost overwhelming succession, but seasoned, to prevent any flagging of the appetite, with a more than generous sprinkling of quips and puns. Of almost every prominent personality who figured in the Crimean theatre of war he has some more or less credible anecdote to tell or some conversation to report in which, needless to say, the writer himself invariably has the last word.

So it is not surprising that, if we are to believe Soyer's own account, the 'final and most difficult undertaking' of his 'Culinary Campaign,' the centre-piece and crowning glory of his activities in the Crimea, was a supper-party which he determined to give in celebration of the end of hostilities. In order to present to his fifty distinguished guests, among them the Chief of Staff and other general officers, a worthy *fête champêtre* on the barren rocks of Cathcart's Hill, every effort was made to transform Soyer's own mud-hut, 'Villarette' (which was barely large enough to hold the company), with wreathes and festoons of flowers into a 'perfumed bosquet.' Outside, a garden of billiard

Opening of Soyer's field kitchen before Sebastopol

table size was splendidly illuminated with lamps fed by ration fat, and a posse of soldiers could be seen, a few hours before the arrival of the guests, painting the parched yellow tufts of grass with a pot of opal green colour so effectively 'that the horses picketed near were actually taken in and played all manner of capers to get loose and have a feed.' As for the supper itself, which lasted until five o'clock in the morning, it was all that could be desired. 'A triumph of culinary art over Crimean resources,' exclaimed *The Times* in a lengthy report on the party which appeared on the Court page, adding that Lord Rokeby himself had 'proposed M. Soyer's health and passed a high eulogium on the services he had rendered to the army by his exertions.'

Soyer's *Culinary Campaign in the Crimea*, published within less than twelve months of his death, was his last effort in the cause he had so much at heart. He had done his work well. He had nourished the army 'as no army was ever fed before.' Already, before the war was over, the grave *Athenaeum* referred to him as 'the male parallel of Miss Nightingale,' and agreed that 'he had a right to claim of reputation that shall be imperishably associated with British prowess in the Crimea.' But it was *Punch* which really did him proud. It declared him worthy of 'an Earldom at least for solacing and strengthening the vitals of the whole army' ; and when Soyer at last returned to England, exhausted and sick with the dreaded Crimean fever, he was welcomed by this poetical effusion headed 'Soyer's Soldiers Friend' :

> The Soldier tired of tough boiled beef,
> Fed worse than any rogue or thief,
> Henceforth shall better fare :
> On fried, and stewed, and roast and boiled,
> And vegetables, cooked, not spoiled,
> By SOYER's art and care.

When he died, just a hundred years ago, on August 5th, 1858, Alexis Soyer could have asked for no finer epitaph.

COMPOSERS IN CLERIHEW

who also wrote the verses

If Rossini
Was no libertine, he
Was certainly one for the girls
With his liquid eyes and his curls.
(Query :
His relations with *L'Italiana in Algieri ?*)

Handel
Thought it an absolute scandal
The way Bach
Cashed in on the *Passions* lark ;
It was always a special yen of his
To compose a setting for *Genesis*.

'Hi ya?'
Said Ravel to de Falla.
'Okay. You well?'
Said de Falla to Ravel :
Neither liked to confess
That he couldn't care less.

It drove Scarlatti
Absolutely batty
To think that what made his
Reputation was *The Good-Humoured Ladies*;
He would far rather have been a
Sort of poor man's Palestrina.

Apparently Johann Strauss
Was an incurable souse.
But can you b-
elieve *The Blue Danube*
Was composed by a guy
Who was perpetually high ?

It was a happy illusion of Brahms
That if he'd exerted his charms
On Jenny Lind
She might well have sinned.
Instead he taught Clara Schumann
That to err was human.

Giuseppi Verdi
Admitted that a bird he
Once saw displaying her garter
Was the inspiration for *Traviata*.
It's only a rumour
That he cribbed the idea from Dumas.

THE PRINCE OF TAILORS

by DONALD MACANDREW
with illustrations from 'The Tailor and Cutter'

LONDON is still the world's sartorial capital. About twenty years ago it ceased to be *de rigueur* that a smart woman's frocks be made in the Rue de la Paix, but the old world's remaining Kings and Maharajahs, and the new world's millionaires, continue to get their suits in Savile Row. And for the same reason that they send their sons to Eton.

Our supremacy dates from 1846. In that key year James Poole, who, starting from scratch, had built up one of London's foremost military tailors, died, having appointed his brilliant son Henry his successor. Henry, who was the original of Mr Vigo in Disraeli's novel, *Endymion*, made Poole's the world's leading tailors. He is responsible for the present one- and two-storied premises in Savile Row, on the plain white stucco façade of which his name, surmounted by a big, battered red and gold crown, is still inscribed. It may be owing to James Poole that a tiny residential backwater in Mayfair comprising Savile Row, Old Burlington Street and Cork Street became eventually, what it still is, the acropolis of the world's tailoring trade. But the high temple on that acropolis was put there by Henry Poole.

Still, James Poole laid the foundations. It was in 1812 that this sometime mantuamaker of Baschurch, Salop, started a small draper's shop in Everett Street, Brunswick Square. He had lately married a widow, not very young. But Poole sought solider virtues in a wife than youth with its soon-liquidated gold, and it was thanks to his dear Mary's sterling assets that he had at long last bid Shropshire good-bye, and opened this new business in London.

Three years later he chanced on another windfall. In February, 1815, Napoleon escaped from Elba. England was panic-stricken, and men from all ranks were quickly mobilized to resist a possible invasion. Poole joined a Volunteer Corps whose members had to provide their own equipment. Though unpractised in tailoring, he and his dear Mary cut and stitched his tunic, making such a good job of it that the first day on parade it caught an officer's eye. 'Are you a tailor, Private Poole?' 'Er—Yessir.' 'Care to make me a tunic, Private Poole?'

'Do my best, sir.' And by the time of Waterloo Poole was so flooded by orders that he resolved to set up as a military tailor. As such, his business forged ahead. By 1822 he opened a big emporium in Regent Street, and in 1823, retaining this, he made his headquarters No. 4 Old Burlington Street.

Old Burlington Street adjoins Savile Row, in those days the street of the surgeons. Only Poole's stables abutted their territory. But it was enough. The advent of this mere cloth-cutter so exacerbated the distinguished cutters of flesh and bone that one and all took wing to found a new colony in Harley Street. Whereupon other tailors moved into the surgeons' houses. The locality suited them because it linked the two recognized streets of their calling, namely, Conduit Street and Sackville Street. The whole area was now the Golden Mile of the Tailors. Yet only their brass plates announced that these prim Georgian frontages were in reality shop fronts.

Three little Pooles were born in Everett Street : James, Mary Ann, and Henry, of whom we treat. Henry George Poole's birthdate was November 8, 1814.

Old Poole, like any other rich tradesman paterfamilias, decided each child's future in infancy. He had associations with the Stock Exchange, so his eldest boy, Jim, became a merchant and a broker. Henry went into the shop. Adelaide and Fanny, Mrs. Poole's grand-daughters by her first marriage, were wed in their 'teens to tailors in Hanover Square and Clifford Street, respectively ; and for his own daughter he no doubt made similar plans. But if so he had to abandon them. Mary Ann grew up plain and gauche and giggly. All her days her handsome brother Henry was to be the sun of Mary Ann's life. When, at fifteen, Henry left the Academy for Noblemen's and Gentle-men's sons which he had attended, to live in the back shop in Old Burlington Street and work in the front shop, her joy brimmed over.

Like all novices, Henry started in the sewing-room. Afterwards, a trimmer taught him how silk facings should be put on, how to flat braid a coat, cord an edge, pad a lapel. Which mastered, he passed on to the cutting-room.

Next, in prosecution of his studies, the fitting department took Henry in hand. Armed with scraps of paper, chalk, and a jotting book, he stood by while the head fitter passed the tape down a customer's groin. But not until he himself was a head fitter did his true genius emerge. The tailor's professional manner Henry had, supposedly, on tap. He knew by instinct how to be at once urbane and deferential, easy without being familiar, ingratiating but not obsequious, and to maintain this at dead level till the client was smiled out of the shop. But Henry had acquired another gift, a freemasonry with some of the more sporting clients. The younger men talked to Henry, involuntarily, as to an acquaintance formed at a meet of the Four-in-Hand Club, a lawn meet, in Tattersall's yard. Many had, in fact, first met him at such assemblages.

This 'horseyness' dated from his schooldays. The other boys had mostly been the sons of great territorial magnates and men in public life, and Henry, to his mama's intense pride, had soaked up a taste for gentlemanly pursuits. Today, at twenty, he drove his mail phaeton in Hyde Park, and was in the first flight with at least three near-London hunts. These circumstances gave old Poole to think. Henry, he knew, though deeply versed in the science of tailoring, would never make a practical tailor. The counting house was ruled out, as the boy had no head for figures : his young cousin Samuel Cundey, the new superintendent, must do the books. Still, old Poole remembered that lucky hap by virtue of which his own hidden genius had been deployed. If Henry, clad in the firm's finest products, were to frequent places where young nobs congregated and, as far as might be, mingle with these, how gloriously history might repeat itself !

This scheme put so much money in the till that old Poole actually listened to one of his son's eager projects for the firm. Henry wanted him to open a sporting department. In those days, it should be explained, men of the calibre of Poole's more distinguished clients were seldom measured or tried on at the shop. Fittings took place in the patron's London home, or, were he an Army man, at the barracks. With the advent of the railway, a country house was frequently the venue. A Meltonian swell would have his tailor's first hand, with a team of cutters and fitters, down at his hunting box for ten days at a time, while his new Jemmy style hunting togs were being constructed. Henry was confident that with his social flair, his charm, his knowledge of the world and of horseflesh, he would be the very man for the job.

Well, it seemed that he was. Youths he met in the field unhesitatingly invited him to their country seats, where he mixed with his host and the bachelor guests, as an equal. Married men, of course, had to be warier ; for them young Snip was labelled, irrevocably, tradesman, and as such dined and wined in the housekeeper's room.

PORTRAIT GALLERY OF BRITISH COSTUME
July 1870
3 Published with the "TAILOR AND CUTTER" by John Williamson 93, Drury Lane London W

Dickens and Disraeli as tailor's models

[173]

Clubland, and bachelor *ménages*, then, acknowledged Henry ; but aristocratic drawing-rooms remained closed to him.

Such husbands as did receive him were mostly great merchant princes and Hebrew money-kings : Rothschild, Levy, Behrens, Bischoffscheim, Montefiore ; persons with whom society's upper crust, in the 1840's, didn't mix. There was, however, an exception. The young Earl of Stamford and Warrington, a vast hereditary landowner, had lately disgusted everybody by marrying a circus-rider. Only sporting men of the more raffish kind ever visited the Stamfords. Among these the lovely pariah countess found Henry gossipy and gay, and a great help when it came to organizing beanfeasts for the stable lads ; while the Earl, who was then M.F.H. of the Albrighton, admired him as a hard man over a country. Two anecdotes about Henry's visits to this noble pair are, perhaps, revealing.

Once, after he had enjoyed their hospitality, a famous wit asked who else had been there. 'Oh, a mixed lot,' replied Henry ; 'Very mixed.' 'Come, come, Pooley,' was the rejoinder, 'we can't all be tailors.' But Henry was still callow when that happened. The second story has him rebuking puppyishness in another. He was playing billiards after supper when his opponent, a mere boy, complained that his coat, made by Poole, was 'a dooced bad fit.' At once Henry seized the chalk and covered the coat with lines and crosses. 'Take it to my shop when you're back in Town and they'll put you right.' And the silly cub was streaked in white for the rest of the evening.

Henry's best friend was Jem Mason, the rough-rider. Son of a well-known Huntingdonshire coper, who jobbed horses to bigwigs all over the country, Jem, at twenty-three, had made racing history by winning the first Aintree Grand National on a horse called Lottery. Since then he had been an international 'lion' on the flat, and on steeplechase courses. But in 1844 he discarded the silk to keep a stud of hunters with Henry at the Bell Inn, Winslow. Here Henry and Jem supplied remounts to followers of the Queen's Buckhounds. And thenceforward the two men were almost inseparable. Out with the Buckhounds, with the Baron de Rothschild's pack, at Ascot, in the crush-room of the Royal Opera House, their slim figures, on which Poole's coats so elegantly sat, were a familiar sight.

In contrast to the handsome, larkish Jem was another keen man to hounds, that 'political sharper' the Pretender to the throne of Imperial France. To many, Prince Louis Napoleon might seem a moody little dago, who had no chance whatever of restoring the Bonaparte dynasty. But when he spoke of his high destiny, his Star, the dull eyes shone. Prince Louis had the visionary's power of igniting his hearers. More, he could charm open their purses. Henry and his friend, the Baron Meyer de Rothschild, between them advanced him some £10,000. One day the impossible must happen, and the Prince, after escapes and risks and surprise sorties unbelievable, would, by a concatenation of flukes, be proclaimed Emperor Napoleon III. On that day, he promised, his creditors would all be repaid and offered posts at the Imperial Court.

Already Henry cut, it will be seen, a conspicuous figure in many societies, all just off the fringe of the best society. Up and up shot the firm's profits, till at last even long-established tailors—Stultz ; Jackson's ; Davis's—decided to follow wherever Poole's led. Old Poole could not but be dazzled by his brilliant son. He deemed it natural that Gentleman Henry should break with the old family pattern of life : namely, hard work all the week, and on Sunday three times to church, roast mutton, early bed. Mary Ann, of course, imitated her favourite brother. Towards the end old Poole's chief solace, other than his dear Mary, was, it seems, his eldest boy, Jim. Jim who had weak lungs now lived permanently with his parents. And Jim predeceased his father by three years.

When, in 1846, Henry inherited Poole's, he at once began altering and enlarging the premises. He made the private door that had hitherto done duty as a main entrance the staff's exit, the clientele being now ushered in from Savile Row by a commissionaire. Then he had the stables pulled down and a big ground floor showroom erected on their site. This formed part of the flat-roofed Italianate building we know today. At that period it had tall, heavily escutcheoned stained glass windows, through which, on illumination nights—royal birth-days, etc.—£300 worth of gaslight streamed, transforming the shop into a genie's palace. The interior glowed with a quasi-Renaissance opulence. When the 1851 Exhibition closed, Henry bought many of its ornate bronze mirrors and statues and vases, which he disposed about the showroom, between pillars and in niches. A balustrade ran the length of one wall. Behind this loomed the 'Peers' Gallery' where many a dignitary stored his regalia in the interim of functions. Here were samples of the new style court dress in bottle-green or mulberry velvet, which James Poole had designed in 1839, and which, encasing

Napoleon III in fur beaver surtout, silk fronts, velvet collar, braid edges. The Prince Imperial in Cambridge style coat in grey tweed. Count Benedetti wears the Benedetti wrapper, silk collar, edgings of broad silk braid. 1869

headless figures, were displayed in enormous glass coffins. Nearby coffins held the ceremonial adjuncts, sword knots, cocked hats, sashes.

But Henry's real aim was to make Poole's primarily sporting tailors. To this end he aligned his front showcases with stalking capes and shooting jackets, with here and there a scarlet hunting frock and riding breeches of white or lavender doe or buckskin or kid. Drawers once sacred to regimental stars and aiglets were now filled with the different hunt buttons. The army uniforms he moved to the far end of the showroom, peopling the middle distance with dress coats, morning coats and all kinds of greatcoat, taglionis, sacs, reefers, raglans, chesterfields. In the basement were stock rooms and pattern rooms, also the world-acclaimed livery department. This last multiplied Poole's Warrants of Appointment. Footmen tricked out by Poole in brimstone and ruby loafed like great golden carp in half the palace entrance halls of Europe, and made the Hyde Park drive from mid-May to July blaze like a bed of Dutch tulips. Poole's decreed Kersey or swansdown smalls for house servants, breeks of drab cord or tricot for carriage servants. And behold Poole's ordinance was observed.

But the splendour he permitted a grandee's retinue was in inverse ratio to what he allowed the potentate himself. Just as Brummell, some three decades earlier, had divested the Prince Regent's friends of their colourful plumage, so Henry Poole, in this key year 1846, drained the blue from the coats, the white from the pantaloons which the d'Orsay clique had made fashionable. But he left their style untouched. He retained the long swallowtail coats, the slender strapped trousers. And when, three years later, the Singer sewing machine came in, he ignored the Yankee innovation. He was, then, assuredly, no rebel. Rather he petrified and embalmed the mode which he found. After which, he locked Tailordom itself in a Sleeping Beauty spell. The exterior of each tailoring house, said Henry Poole, should proclaim the good manners within. A man's tailor should be to him as his family solicitor, or his doctor ; he should drop in casually as into his club. Eschew, therefore, all advertisement, gold letters, window display. For a bespoke tailor the correct form is opaque glass windows, dimness.

Again, in matters of administration, Henry was a power. Every tailor adopted his out-of-work fund for his staff, also his Sick and Burial Society, though not one could afford, as Henry could, to double the sum each man had subscribed to this out of his own pocket. Further, they copied his 'task system' of wages. By this the hands were paid according to the amount of work done and not by time, and had orders flowed in evenly the whole year round all would have been well. As it was, ructions followed—but not in 1846. In 1846 Poole's was Tailordom's lodestar. Only one man, the world said, in 1846, could influence Henry Poole. Jem Mason, apart from his Turf celebrity, enjoyed wide acclaim as a dandy. His seraphically cut coats, his nonpareil petershams, were, as all London knew, Poole-manufactured. Did Jem never pay his bills? Then Henry would dress him free for the advertisement. The 'greatest cross-country rider of all time' would be his impresario, his fashion-plate.

Jem's sway over Henry resulted, about 1857, in an offshoot to the sporting department. A crop of six tiny gilt fitting cubicles, satin-lined, in an annexe to the showroom, was the first indication of this : a horse dummy complete with horse block, the second. But only with the harnessing of Bucephalus was his purpose revealed. For his saddle had three pommels, a flat cantle, a quilted seat : a lady's saddle. Poole's had started a new line as *lady's* habitmaker. The tremendous vogue of female horsemanship in mid-Victorian times has been ascribed to the expansion of the crinoline. Immersed in a silken bell-tent nine yards round at the base and a flowing sacque, a girl's figure and a stout matron's were as one. Thrice welcome then (to girls) the Nereid-like habit which clung so tight it had to be sewn over the client's bare skin. Once it was on, Poole's assistants would hoist the fair client on to Bucephalus. Ah! Bust wants filling out. Horsehair wadding, I think, and a piece cut on the cross let into the back of the bodice. Skirt falls to a point in correct classic folds. Thank you, Madam. Madam may dismount now.

These assistants were not, of course, culled from the hundred men employed in Henry's King Street workshop, nor yet from those operating in Savile Row. To dress the *Amazone à la Mode 1857* he had engaged a dozen young ladies. And to superintend these a competent forewoman. Emma Walker, a draper's daughter, had lately been in charge of the saleswomen at Holbrook's, the Bond Street glove shop, of which firm, patronized by royalty, her brother Edward was general manager. Patently she had first-rate credentials. Yet she stayed at Poole's less than two years. For, early in 1859, when he was forty-five and she forty-one, Henry married Emma, thus obliging her to retire to Dorset Cottage, his Thames-side retreat at Fulham, where lived her female in-laws. How, one wonders, did old Mrs Poole react to Emma? Henry had observed tradition by marrying into the clothiery trade, yes, but where pray was Emma's dowry? Well, well, she and Mary Ann must try to like her. For Henry was seldom at home nowadays. Almost nightly he supped with his bang-up friends at that odious

Princess Marie Louise and the Marquis of Lorne. 1870

Blue Posts in Cork Street : his hunting stud at Greenford claimed him most Saturdays : he collected water-colours, French furniture, old violins. At last, after six stultifying months, Emma had her elder sister Eliza, a confirmed invalid, to live with her at Dorset Cottage.

When, three years later, old Mrs Poole died, her half-share in Poole's former establishment, No. 171 Regent Street, a big Indian shawl warehouse, reverted to Mary Ann. Mary Ann and her step-nieces

Adelaide and Fanny became the joint proprietors. But Mary Ann's part of the takings was all at Henry's disposal. Unlike his malcontent wife, Henry's sister saw divinity in everything he did. Oh, those rare evenings when Henry dined at home and one listened, tranced, imparadised, while he discoursed of his noble patrons, his friends ! Ecstasy to give, give all, to so flaming a brother.

In 1860 Henry gained another scalp. One night the Prince of Wales went to the Princess's Theatre to see Fechter in *Ruy Blas*, and admired the elegant cut of the actor's coat. After the performance, Fechter told him it was a Poole's commodity. Thenceforward H. Poole & Co. furnished the chief part of the Prince's wardrobe.

Until now, although Henry had clothed two-thirds of the *beau-monde*, he himself had always been kept a stone's throw outside its perimeter. To reach its centre was Henry's life aim. Prince Louis, thanks largely to sums advanced him by Henry Poole and certain Jew financiers, was now Napoleon III of France. Henry knew that H.R.H. of Wales and his companions were mostly deep in debt. Also that a few Rothschilds, Levis, Montefiores, had entered H.R.H.'s planet group by way of letters of credit, overdrafts, loans. Well, Poole's had its long credit system, a system which might be extended . . . indefinitely. . . . Soon the firm was despatching tens of thousands of pounds-worth of goods each year to the Prince's circle.

II

Every day in the Season found Henry—but not Emma—in Rotten Row at the fashionable hour. Here all the *ton*, whose movements the *Morning Post* so assiduously chronicled, was on view in full fig from twelve to one. From the Achilles statue to Kensington Gardens a choppy, glinting sea of thoroughbred horses and well-bred riders, well-cut habits and well-blocked tall hats, rose and fell continuously, while an endless verge of sleek 'chimney-pots' and frock coats pressed five deep against the palings. For Henry the whole park was a gallery exhibiting his creations. Had not thousands of these flitting shapes been snip-snapped into elegance on Poole's cutting boards ?

His breasting this main resembled a royal progress ; for though the swirls and eddies and cross-currents of horsemen didn't part at his approach, he was exchanging salutes right and left at every step. Presently he descried Jem Mason. Jem's riding school was now at

Mount Street, Mayfair. At forty-six he was still 'tall, thin and smart as paint' and 'Poole'd up to the eyes' in his 'black coat and doeskin breeches, soft and supple as a lady's glove.' Ambling about the Park together, the two friends could now criticize each rider in sight, his seat in the pigskin, the build of his coat, the hang and the fall of the riding habits. Upon such minutiae the horsey tailor and the dandy horse-dealer were alike connoisseurs.

Here, for instance, was General Lord Cardigan who, eight years earlier, had led the Balaclava charge. The veteran warrior was riding his grey charger in the now antiquated high school style of equitation : toes in the stirrups, long stirrup leathers, heels down, legs from the knee carefully clear of the horse's sides ; and he wore, much padded, his Master of the Cavalry's uniform. Less elegant, far, was his countess. Tugging at her horse's mouth and clad in the 'sapphire velveteen Hussar's pelisse with fourteen gilt buttons' and the huge 'Astrakhan busby with plume' that H. Poole & Co. had, reluctantly, made for her, Lady Cardigan was ogling all the personable young men. Henry merely nodded. And Jem cut her dead. Yet the next minute saw them hailing enthusiastically another social leper, another countess riding with her husband.

How Henry loved his dear Stamfords ! The Earl was now M.F.H. of the Quorn, and had lately inducted him into the cream of hunting in High Leicestershire. As to Kitty Stamford, she was wearing today 'a hortensia blue twilled Elysian beaver habit, amethyst velvet facings . . . gauntlets . . . a François 1st. hat.' A most finished get-up. *Too* finished, said passing ladies. Stagey. Like her equestrianism, her rising from the saddle in such perfect time to the cadence of her horse's steps ; one positively *smelt* the circus ring. But Henry marked how becomingly a Poole's confection sat on this tall, shy, black-eyed histrionic *ecuyère*. A moment later a noisy group of horsemen accosted him. What a contrast ! A. J. Lewis, the Regent Street linen-draper who painted battle pieces and followed crack hunts : Millais and Fred Walker, the artists : the novelist Anthony Trollope : Bartley the Oxford Street bootmaker : André, the Bond Street hatter. So Rabelaisian the jokes, so gusty and prolonged the laughter, that Henry was lifted far above Rotton Row with its feuds and its cliqueyness.

As soon as the group broke up he was re-immersed. All about him now were the children of the aristocracy : youths who all doffed their hats : girls who, like the goddesses on bas-reliefs, seemed forever in profile, for in 1862 etiquette still forbade them to bow to their habit-maker in public. However, it was the toilettes of the 'goddesses' that attracted Henry. Lady Violet Greville's 'violet diagonal habit' : Lady Jocelin's 'ophelia dingle cloth habit, dragonet braids' : Princess Czartoryska's 'black vicuna, embossed crowsfeet olivettes.' These he saw as he rode round the Row. Then, having made his tour of inspection, he set his horse's head for the Stanhope Gate, judging it best to return to business before fashion ebbed from the Park.

'Poole's,' says a memoirist, 'was a great rendezvous for gilded and sporting youth.' It was 'more like a club than a shop.' Behind the showroom and lit by giant bronze candelabra was 'the Parlour,' whither, from 3.30 p.m. to 5, flocked many of the Lords Dundreary and Tomnoddy from Rotten Row, to sip Pooley's mons'ous fine clar't and hock, and puff Pooley's cigars. 'The firm's well-known trio of high priests, Mr Cundey (General Supervisor), Mr Dent (Coats) and Mr Allen (Trousers)' we are told, 'frequently joined the convivial gathering.'

But before they shut up shop Messrs. Supervisor, Coats and Trousers may well have exchanged looks. The Chief *was* going it on social contacts. Hm'mm ! Those drinks. And those Havannahs. Hm'mm ! *Some* clients were being allowed prodigious long-term credits, *weren't* they ? And the Prince of Wales and his gang were obtaining barouch-loads of goods scot free.

III

Each year Henry—but not Emma—crossed the Channel to visit his friend, the Emperor Napoleon III. Usually he was invited in late autumn, when the Imperial Court was at Compiègne.

Here elaborate follies, charades, and paper-chases were the order of the day. Or the Empress might solicit Henry to play the piano or sing. Most memorable he found the big bi-weekly stag hunts in the forest. The Imperial Venery was for him, like Rotten Row, chiefly a dress parade of his own wares.

The Meet was always held in a large clearing, two kilometres from the château, whence eight broad alleys rayed out to the forest's distances. A fanfare of horns ushered in the Imperial cortège. At its head rode the Chief Ranger of Compiègne, le Baron de Wimpferen, in a 'rifle green jacket with gold lace, a laced tricorne hat, cockfeathers, doeskins, jackboots.' Then came the Emperor's break, drawn by six

The Prince of Wales in single-breasted slate-coloured frock coat in plain Levantine with silk fronts ; the Duke of Edinburgh in single-breasted quilted morning coat, with double-breasted waistcoat and check angola trousers ; and Prince Victor. 1870

horses. The team's collars were a-jingle with bells, a fox's brush dangled from each ear, and a postilion in periwig and buckskins (by Poole) bestrode each saddle. The little weary-eyed Emperor, the nimrods in his suite, and the long line of chasseurs who drove in four-horse carriages in his wake, all, like the Chief Ranger, wore green and gold Louis Quatorze uniforms tailored by Poole : Poole's hand was also revealed in many of the orthodox scarlet or black coats of those followers who, in two-horse carriages, succeeded the Hunt Members, and again, among the drag-loads of well-dressed lookers-on. At the *carrefour*, a hemicycle of *piqueurs*, with huge trumpets encircling their shoulders, waited by a big bonfire : also, another of kennelmen, each holding eight couple of English hounds on a leash : while a third crescent of grooms stood to attention by the party's mounts. To Henry was allotted an Irish liver chestnut from the Emperor's stables.

While they were drinking stirrup cup, a fat, pale young man with blue bubbly eyes and a blasé look rode up to Henry and conversed with him languidly. Henry was in transports. Ever since he had had the Prince of Wales' Warrant of Appointment in 1863 he had been collecting such nods as it pleased H.R.H. to accord him in Hyde Park. And now, here in France, his tip-top catch was publicly befriending him. The Prince's pink cut-away coat and white leathers made a pretext for mutual congratulation and, presently, laying a genial hand on Henry's shoulder, the royal patron led his tailor to where a group of horsemen surrounded a tiny basket chaise with Shetland ponies. In it, holding the ribbons, sat the Empress Eugénie, now in the late afternoon of her beauty, and beside her, as fair as may blossom, the young Princess of Wales. . . . Too soon did the horns sound the *débouche* for the take-off.

To a blast of trumpets the unleashed hounds poured down a grassy ride, the splendidly decked horsemen at their heels : the notes died, the entire field scattered. Then a single horn rang out. Brazen-throated, jubilant, it sang its mounting song, and as it ceased, others at the forest's outskirts, in its lairs, and thrilling down each aisle of patriarchal oaks, took up the tune : the stag, uncarted in another *carrefour*, had been viewed fleeting through patches of sunlight and shadow. Each incident of the hunt was thus marked by traditional calls. There was the *Appel*, the wild *Hallali*, the *St. Hubert*, the dirge-like *Retraite ;* the chase was an extravaganza, an operatic mime, performed in the music-shot forest. But the sport—the sport was a farce. Like all his countrymen, Henry missed what was called at Melton 'a clinking run.' If there was no plough, there was also no grassland ; there were no breath-taking gallops across open country, no oxers, no flying fences, no icy brooks to clear. So, too, with the homeward procession. The setting sun gilded the forest, intensifying the scarlet of the Englishmen's coats, while the Imperial uniforms went dim as the ivy that swaddled the huge-boled trees. Courtiers from some tapestry by le Brun moved through a golden landscape by Claude. But nobody's coat was muddy, nobody larked home or sang. All was as different as could be from a long hack home in the Shires.

Alike in its pageantry and its poor sport the *Grand Chasse* was typical Second Empire : an over-lustrous glaze coating metal intrinsically sham. Cracked, riveted, the eggshell régime must soon break into a thousand splinters. Still, bright fugitive colours and fancy dress can be great fun when one is on holiday. Unluckily this year—1866—Henry's holiday was cut short by an S.O.S. from the Master Tailor's Association, of which he was the chairman. The workers, headed by Poole's foremen, had threatened to strike. Would Henry please come home and deal with them ?

IV

Before he went abroad, Poole's men had moved for higher wages on the plea that under the 'task system' their earnings, even in the busy season, could scarcely exceed 6d. an hour. In view of the slack time in winter, they wanted him so to raise the prices of his goods as to guarantee an average workman 7d. an hour. Henry had submitted their memorial to his association. But with it he had brought a new log, one that increased the cost of some articles of dress and reduced others. Fifty London tailors were to present this to their staffs the next day. Accept this, they were to say, or you go. But the men complained that under the new tariff they were worse off than before. What now recalled Henry was word of a meeting of two thousand working tailors held to resist it. Henry saw he must act quickly. Accordingly he wired his agents all over Europe to send foreign journeymen should the need arise, and then consented to receive a deputation of operative tailors. These handed him their ultimatum ; accept it, said they, or we go.

Henry just glanced at their list, and tore it up. *He* to be coerced by his work-people ! Fantastic ! Next day he closed shop, confident that he could starve the recalcitrants into compliance. Five years earlier he could have done so. But not today. The men from the Continent never turned up ; nor did any of his outworkers. The Committee of the Operative Tailors' Protective Association had been able, like

" Dꝶ Livingstone I presume ! "

PORTRAIT GALLERY OF BRITISH COSTUME

October 1872

Published with the 'TAILOR AND CUTTER' by John Williamson 93 Drury Lane London W.C.

Dr Livingstone wears a dahlia-coloured velvet beaver frock coat, velvet cuffs and fronts, edges braided with velvet. H. M. Stanley wears a belted poncho wrapper himself, to telegraph to agents in Paris, Brussels, Hamburg, Berlin, and Vienna, bidding them send nobody to London in the present crisis. Fifty London master tailors had organized lock-outs, yes ; but two thousand journeymen tailors were on strike, certain of the co-operation of their fellow craftsmen all over Europe. Henry's aristocratic unconcern had tripped him up. The high disdain that had bleared his eyes to the incidence of the sewing machine had also blinkered them to these still newer-fangled trades union societies, which were now, it seemed, the depositories of unlimited funds. Power had shifted from the boss to the employee. And he had never known !

Ten days passed. Then Henry hit on a compromise. Payment must still be made by the garment and not by time, but with a minimum piece price of 6d. an hour. This would not give the men quite all they asked for, and yet they must gain by it. In addition, he promised to introduce two sewing machines into his workshop. True, these were only to do inside work—sleeve-linings, pocket-linings, etc.—but the men would be paid for half what the machines did. As the machines worked quickly they must make on this too. Almost at once Poole's men accepted the terms. The others, as usual, followed suit.

The Chief's handling of this affair elicited paeans of praise from Messrs. Supervisor, Coats and Trousers. Nor was this the only time his *savoir-faire* had impressed them. Once an irate customer had entered the shop on horseback to complain about the fit of some riding breeches: too tight at the fork and the kneepan, damn you ! Too baggy everywhere else : and he waved the offending garment, causing his steed to shy and Poole's men to duck behind the counters. It had taken the Chief one second to grasp the bridle and put mount and man to the rightabout. That was the Chief all over. Prompt. Authoritative.

But no business head. Tell him about the drop in the firm's profits, and his manner became far-off at once. And the profits *were* falling. Just as the names in the bad debts ledger were mounting steadily.

The War of 1870, which altered the map of Europe, synchronized in London with a social readjustment. The Second Empire was no more, but its departing spirit had been captured by the Prince of Wales, who modelled his circle on the easy-going cosmopolite court of Napoleon III. Rothschild, Levi, Montefiore, etc., now mixed with ambassadors and duchesses at Marlborough House. So did Henry. In the century's early seventies, and his own late fifties, he was at last *persona grata* not only with patrician men, but with their wives.

From 1870–74 the shop scarcely saw him. In the smart sporting cosmos, however, he was much remarked. The Duke of Portland, then Master of the Horse, acclaimed Henry's mount one of the three most beautiful in the Row, and Lord Lonsdale relates how he used often to accompany Henry in his phaeton 'drawn by two of the best horses in London—each had a white sock—a celebrated pair.' Then for the Boat Race each year he 'entertained a large party which often included the Prince of Wales.' On these occasions, Henry's private steam launch, decked out in flags, and freighted with his magnificent guests, would follow the crews up the river, after which they were regaled with 'a truly sumptuous luncheon' at Dorset Cottage. Properly, of course, Emma should have acted hostess at these repasts. She never did. And Mary Ann declined, too. Henry had lately bought another, larger, house on the Marine Parade, Kemp Town, Brighton, and his 'harem' made this their bolt-hole from the London Season.

Yet Henry would have been pleased to take Emma into Society, for she was handsome in a strong-featured way—a rather less equine George Eliot—and dignified in her plain black alpaca dresses made from material supplied by the firm. But the idea revolted her. Always she had distrusted Henry's friends.

Then a catastrophe threw husband and wife together. Henry had an apoplectic fit. Through all the long months of exhaustion, of spasms and comas that followed it, Emma nursed him indefatigably, jealously. Early in 1876 he appeared to mend. One gusty day in mid-April he drove his phaeton along the seafront, and was caught some distance from Kemp Town in a snowstorm. . . . After a fortnight's relapse, a second violent attack, lasting ten hours, killed him. He was buried in the family vault at Highgate Cemetery.

V

With Henry's death, liabilities poured in. Ten thousand pounds had to be written off as bad debts. Emma, in the twelvemonth she survived him, had to part with horses, equipages, water-colours, French furniture, everything. Even so, there remained heavy encumbrances. Samuel Cundey, the new principal, talked of selling the concern lock, stock and barrel at a low valuation.

But Mary Ann wouldn't hear of it. To avert a crash she not only paid all her dividends back into the firm, but purchased from her step-

This plate was issued with THE TAILOR AND CUTTER *in 1872, and, although her name is not given, the lady is undoubtedly Catherine Walters, the famous courtesan known as 'Skittles.' Henry Poole supplied her with riding habits free, for advertisement*

Prince Leopold, wearing a two-buttoned worsted coat and military drab trousers, hair-lined. Prince Arthur wearing a coat like a small sac, with four patch pockets and waist-belt, and knickerbockers in Shetland tweed, heather mixture. 1871

nieces Adelaide and Fanny their half-share in No. 171 Regent Street, with a view to selling the business outright and paying the net profits into Poole's. Thus did Mary Ann preserve Henry's house. The saviour of Poole's was Mary Ann. Yet on her death, three years later, a small sum was left in her will to a lost dogs' home, a charity that had caught at the old spinster's heart in her last years.

Meantime, Samuel Cundey had contrived to make certain of the *jeunesse dorée* settle their accounts. Henry Poole might allow the Prince of Wales and his associates unlimited tick, but Cousin Samuel was more radical in spirit. Friends of the Prince or no, said he roundly, they must pay. When bills poured into Marlborough House, H.R.H. was vexed. Tradesmen should be content with the privilege of royal and lordly custom and not so far forget themselves as to think of their dues. Could Cundey not double his prices for his less exalted patrons ? Make the solvent pay for the insolvent, good heavens ? Other firms did it. But Cundey went on, imperturbably, pressing for payment. Whereupon the Prince, in a pet, withdrew his household's patronage.

Still, Samuel had nearly every other European crowned head on his books, besides Asiatic potentates eager to Europeanize themselves. And when, in 1883, young Howard Cundey continued, the business pulled round magnificently. The premises were again enlarged. Royal Warrants multiplied. Branches were opened in Paris, Vienna, Berlin. Most important, in Poole's showroom a third and last transformation scene was effected.

Upon the vivid regimental and hunting coats which had made the big showing at Poole's in its first dynasty the sun now set, while clouds of plain subfusc material took their place. Poole's became chiefly, what it had always been in part, a civil tailors. Scarlet and buckskins vanished about 1900, scarlet and gold braid some ten years earlier. As to ladies' riding habits, they had barely survived Henry Poole. Those two outsize Dianas, the Empress Elizabeth of Austria and her sister the ex-Queen Marie of Naples, were, in the year Henry died, among the last to mount Bucephalus.

Henry Poole's legacy to us is the standardization of men's town clothes. He halted the march of men's fashions. Today, on all formal occasions—christenings, weddings, etc.—men wear suits which, till Henry came, were the correct garb only at funerals.

But the fossilization is not quite complete. Nothing, no work of art, is immune from the contemporary microbe, and the contour of a Savile Row suit has noticeably altered in the course of a hundred and ten years. Savile Row itself is infected. An American today, plunging into the criss-cross of quiet lanes which divides Regent Street from Bond Street, may at first think he has stumbled on that late Georgian retreat for distinguished surgeons which it was before the tailors erupted there. Old Burlington Street remains intact, and so, viewed from its Burlington Gardens approach, is Savile Row. True, at the Row's top end he will find the new police station, the Ministry of Health, etc., and, a few yards away, Cork Street, marred by bright new shop fronts. Yet over all, the Henry Poole spell is still thick enough to persuade him he breathes the fumes of privilege, of clubs, of Toryism, which he flew the Atlantic to find.

As in the tailor's citadel, so in their Parthenon. Poole's showroom is the same panelled hypostyle our forefathers knew, its furniture the same massy mahogany tables piled with bolts of dark cloth. The same hush prevails. Facing you as you enter is the same oval portrait of Napoleon III. But tubular strip-lighting now replaces Henry Poole's weighty bronze candelabra. And 'the Peers' Gallery' has gone. Also some of the peers. Poole's relies nowadays, as never before, on overseas custom. That is why so much of the Victorian atmosphere is maintained. Poole's present directors, the late Mr. Howard Cundey's two sons, who have preserved Henry Poole's house and filled it with the eager and imaginative goodwill of themselves and their staff, are providing *quelque chose anglais pour les étrangers.*

Each year, to the plain frontal and rich, dim interior of Poole's come pilgrims white, brown, black and yellow to bespeak suits tailored in all essentials to the Henry Poole formula. The great sartor's edicts still hold. All, all, it seems, wish to be turned out like the English gentleman whose style was fixed—apparently forever—in 1846 by Henry Poole.

The author wishes to express his thanks to Mr Hugh Cundey and Mr Samuel Cundey for their kind assistance in the research required for this essay.

THE PRESIDENT AND I

by CHRISTOPHER SHORT

I W A S once invited to a reception given for President Truman.
That sounds rather good, doesn't it—as if I am accustomed to moving in exalted circles. As a matter of fact, I *am* accustomed to moving in exalted circles. I was once invited to a tea given for Mrs Zulaski by the Daughters of the American Revolution, an organization which, like the French Radical Socialists, is not nearly so Left Wing as it sounds. Don't ask me who Mrs Zulaski was or is. I do not know. I do know, however, that had she not been pretty exalted the Daughters of the American Revolution would not have given a tea for her.

I was once invited, moreover, to a tea given by the Society of Cincinnatus, but I could not go because I had a cold. The Society of Cincinnatus is an organization which mainly caters for those who— because of their sex—do not qualify for membership in the Daughters of the American Revolution. The Daughters of the American Revolution compose a body, 'pride,' or 'figure' of ladies who for the most part are not eligible for the Society of Cincinnatus. You can see, therefore, how important both organizations are.

While I am expatiating on my high life, I may as well mention the fact that I once met Gary Cooper in a wave at Atlantic Beach. I asked him how he liked Atlantic Beach and he replied most civilly that he liked it very much. Had I been a gossip columnist I could have cashed in on this interview, but I have always believed that the great are entitled to their privacy as much as anyone else. I am only mentioning the matter now because it happened such a long time ago that Mr Cooper could not possibly mind, at this late date, my revealing this private detail of his personal life.

I was also once at a literary tea at which the late Charles Morgan was the guest of honour. Mr Morgan was most charming to everyone present, including me, whom he shook warmly by the hand. The sandwiches on this occasion were excellent.

But to return to our muttons, if Mr Truman will forgive the metaphor. The reception to which I was bid in order to meet him (he was then still President) was at the Mayflower Hotel in Washington, D.C. It may have been given by the Daughters of the American Revolution, the Society of Cincinnatus, or the Descendants of Nero ; I do not remember ; nor is the matter important. The important thing is that I was invited.

At the bottom of the invitation there were the words 'Evening Dress.' This put me in a bit of a spot, for my tails had been blitzed by moths, and I did not think it would be respectful to greet the President of the United States in only a black tie, if you see what I mean. I was able to borrow the necessary 'tails' from a friend, however, and although this suit was far too large for me, since he is a veritable giant, I was able to make it do by hitching up the trousers under my armpits and padding my shoulders with newspaper. The whole effect was a bit curious, as the tails hung almost to the ground and the sleeves of the coat were so long that they almost obscured my hands. I looked rather like a circus clown, especially as bow ties show a regrettable tendency on me to look like moths that have been in a battle with a night hawk.

I was so fortunate as to be able to escort to the reception a charming young lady of my acquaintance. Because of the exigencies of time we arranged to meet at the Mayflower. This was perhaps a mistake, since it gave her no time to get used to my appearance before being, as one might say, put on display with me in the Mayflower ballroom. It would have been better if we could have met first under rather subdued lighting, preferably in a nice cosy bar somewhere. The shock would not then have been so great. As it was, the sight of me shuffling across the vast and splendid lobby of the hotel must have made her wonder if she had not by some fantastic accident got herself a date with a gorilla.

Actually it would have made little difference if we had met somewhere else first, since my appearance altered considerably soon after my arrival at the Mayflower—and altered for the worse. As my date rose to greet me, wearing an expression of understandable alarm, and I bowed with old world courtesy over her hand, one of the folded sheets of newspaper which I had pinned as padding for the shoulders of my tail coat escaped from its moorings and fell on the floor.

I looked at it with horror ; my date regarded it with wonderment. Finally I collected my senses enough to pick it up and stuff it in my trouser pocket. 'Bit in it I wanted to save,' I mumbled. 'Very interesting. All about the United Nations.'

This attempt to carry the matter off with sang-froid was not wholly successful, however, since I was conscious that one of my shoulders was now much lower than the other. Desperately I tried to even things up by thrusting my non-padded shoulder upwards, but this only made me appear as if I had been seized with a sudden neuralgia of the neck. I shrugged my shoulders and resigned myself to looking like a fiddler crab.

I could not have made a worse move. Perhaps in the acuteness of my embarrassment I shrugged my shoulders too hard, or perhaps the thing was bound to happen anyway on this ill-fated evening. At any rate, the other piece of newspaper fell out of my coat and unfolded itself on the floor, revealing the headline: *McGinnis Fights Extradition.*

I looked at it with a glazed eye, and my date did too.

'Ah, yes, McGinnis,' I said weakly. 'He's fighting extradition.' I leant down, collected the paper, and stuffed it in my other pocket.

With some trepidation my date took my arm and we proceeded to the ballroom. At the entrance I caught sight of my reflection in a mirror placed there for the convenience of the ladies and the inconvenience of such misfits as myself. I recoiled with horror at what I saw. Without the extra shoulder padding, my coat hung like a cloak on my frame. My hands were invisible and my tails hung down to my heels. My trousers, pulled up the way they were, looked like an illustration by Tenniel of the garb of Tweedledum or Tweedledee. My appearance was alarmingly simian.

There was a man standing next to me, a man whose evening wear was as impeccable as mine was peccable. He was evidently a major-domo of sorts, for as the guests arrived he checked their invitations and called out their names in a loud voice for the benefit of a receiving line in the Grand Ballroom. I saw him regarding my image with almost as much distaste as it evoked in my own breast. I caught his eye in the mirror and became immediately afflicted with that form of hysterical embarrassment which makes one do and say things foreign to one's real nature.

'Orang Utang !' I cried, hopping up and down and flapping my handless arms.

The man drew himself up and stepped to the door. 'Mr and Mrs Orang Utang,' he called. They are used to foreign names in Washington, which is a centre of diplomatic activity.

Inside the ballroom there was a long queue of people waiting to shake hands with the President, who was out of sight in a sort of alcove. I have a weak knee muscle, a relic of an old football injury, which makes standing about difficult for me, and so I decided to forgo the pleasure of meeting Mr Truman in person and made my way to a table on the side of the ballroom floor, where I sank gratefully into a seat. In a little while I was joined by my date, who had been wafted along the tide of protocol and had shaken hands with the President when her turn came. She was quite excited about the event and described with vivacity how charming Mr Truman was and how well he was looking.

'He'll be coming out in a minute,' she said, 'I was almost the last. That is his seat over there.' She pointed to a Presidential Box on a stand that had been constructed farther along on our side of the room, and which was decorated with flags and potted palms. It looked rather a Robinson Crusoeish structure, but I have noticed that visiting dignitaries all over the world—I *have* been around a bit : I once travelled in the same train as the Duke of Windsor—have to submit to being treated as if they were native chieftains with a passion for bright colours and trinkets.

I settled myself to await the arrival of Mr Truman with an agreeable feeling of anticipation, since I had never seen him in person hitherto.

In a few minutes the band struck up 'Hail to the Chief,' an energetic if somewhat incoherent and tuneless fanfare which is always played when the President arrives at places where there is a band. I looked towards the alcove expecting Mr Truman to appear at any instant.

He did appear, but, unfortunately for me, just at the moment when he did, everyone in front of me stood up, and I got no glimpse of him at all. By the time I had hoisted myself and my weak knee on to my feet, he had walked by, and I was unable to see him over the heads of all the people who were straining to watch his progress. I could, however, see the Presidential Box, and I assured myself that I should get a clear view of Mr Truman when he came into it.

I should not have been so optimistic. I might have known that the Gods had stacked the cards against me that evening and held all the aces in a 'no trump' hand. Mr Truman's arrival in the box was preceded by that of his entourage, who all stood along the sides, waiting for the Chief to enter and take his place in the centre. I got an excellent view of the backs of several Cabinet Ministers, but of Mr Truman not even a glint of a white shirt front. Even when they were all seated, the heads of the Cabinet Ministers (always a bit outsize) prevented my seeing beyond the perimeter of the box.

Determined not to be thwarted, I got up and, telling my date that

I would be right back, I strolled out on to the floor of the ballroom and proceeded in as dignified a manner as my awkward garb would allow in the direction of the President. My intention was to amble by and have a casual look without being so rude as to stare.

I had reckoned without those Gods again. I had only gone a short way up the middle of the ballroom floor when I was suddenly picked out by a spotlight and there was a roar of laughter from the assembly. With mounting terror I looked around me and perceived that every eye was fixed upon me. I was the only person on the floor.

It took me but an instant to realize what had happened. There was evidently going to be some sort of a performance, for the amusement of the President and the rest of us, and I had strolled out on to a stage that was set for other, professional, performers. Some wag had picked out my progress with a spotlight and the crowd was obviously under the impression that I was a comic turn. Hastily I retreated to the side-lines. I feel sure that had the attention of the audience not been distracted by a group of tumblers they would have demanded that I go on and finish my act.

Prickling with mortification I crept back to my table, where my date was sitting with rather a bewildered air. She leaned over towards me. 'It's in the other direction—the way we came,' she whispered. My humiliation was complete.

By now it had become a matter of personal honour with me to see President Truman. I determined to have a good look at him even if the Fates and all the forces of the FBI stood in my way. I said as much to my date. With impatience I waited, therefore, while a very good variety entertainment unfolded for the next three-quarters of an hour. I felt sure there would be an intermission. During that pause I planned to go up to the Presidential Box and positively glare at Mr Truman.

In due course the intermission arrived and I and my date pushed our way through the crowd that was converging on the Presidential Rostrum. Finally we emerged at a point from which we could command a clear view of the entire box. People were packed into it like sardines. The President was nowhere to be seen. If he were still there I did not envy him, since he must be in imminent danger of being squeezed to death.

It looked as if I had been foiled again ; but by now my dander was really up. Telling my date to wait a minute I went off to reconnoitre. The box was set off from the rest of the room by a tasselled cord and a row of potted palms and flowers on either side. There was, however, a space of several feet at the back of the box, and I saw that a moderately agile person could climb up on to the stand without any difficulty and might, if he were lucky, be able to see the President on his own level, so to speak.

That I hesitated not a moment shows how my ordinarily mild personality had been inflamed by the humiliations to which my suiting had subjected me that evening, and by the frustration of my attempts to see the President. I slipped under the ropes dividing the box from the rest of the room and in a trice I was ascending the rear of the structure. Nobody would notice me, I figured, since the palm trees hid me from the ballroom, and there was such a crush in the box that no one there would be capable of seeing beyond the end of his nose.

I left the Gods and the FBI out of my calculations. I had just begun my climb when there was a tap on the calf of my leg and I looked down into the face of a gimlet-eyed man in a double-breasted dinner jacket. 'Going somewhere?' he asked politely. He was obviously a guard of some sort, and I put him down in my own estimation as being an FBI man.

I slipped to the ground, endeavouring to stem a mounting nervousness. I realized too late that in the eyes of the forces of the law any odd behaviour in the neighbourhood of a Presidential Box was definitely suspect.

'Just wanted to see the President,' I explained ingratiatingly. 'Been trying to see him all evening.'

The man looked at me coldly. 'He's been around all evening,' he said. "You could have shaken hands with him a while back.'

I felt my nerve going. There is a certain Third Degree force in the very way the Law of any country looks at you. 'I know,' I said lamely, 'but I didn't want to then.'

'But you do now?' he asked, with assumed astonishment.

'No,' I replied heatedly, 'I don't. I just want to see him.'

'About anything in particular?' he inquired, looking at me with grave suspicion.

'No, I only wanted to look at him.'

He regarded me for some minutes in silence, evidently weighing up in his own mind whether I was a dangerous lunatic or just a plain fool. He must have discarded the former category as being inappropriate, for he gave me a sudden charming smile.

[198]

'O.K., Mac,' he said, 'so you just wanted to look at him. Well, that's all right. A lot of people do. But you can't do it this way. You'll have to go round in front. Before you go, though, I'd better just check your invite. It's not that I really suspicion you, but we can't be too careful.'

With a feeling of relief I reached into my pocket for the invitation that would prove my right to be there. He was evidently not such a bad guy after all. Good old FBI. As he had pointed out, their responsibility was too great to take any risks. I might easily be a crank, or worse, who had slipped into the party undetected and was trying to get at the President. Anyway, my invitation would clear that up. It would show him that I had been invited by The Nephews of Napoleon, or whoever it was. It would fix . . . where the heck *was* that invitation?

Frantically I searched through the pockets of my coat and waistcoat, removing their contents and putting them hastily back when the missing invitation was not found amongst them. The FBI agent looked at me sardonically. In desperation I started going through my trouser pockets. Of course, the first thing I brought out was one of the pieces of newspaper. The FBI man's eyebrows lifted. Hurriedly I crammed it back. Then, thoughtlessly, I pulled out the second sheet from my other pocket.

This was too much for him.

'Let's have a look at that," he said flatly, holding out his hand, evidently thinking that he might find in the paper some clue to my eccentric behaviour.

'It's nothing,' I said, as I handed it to him, 'I just had it in my coat.'

'*McGinnis Fights Extradition,*' he read out. 'Friend of yours, huh?'

'No, no,' I expostulated, 'I never heard of him before.'

'Then why are you carrying around a newspaper clipping about him? Or is this the bit you are keeping : *Murderer Still at Large*?'

I can see now that he was probably teasing me in his quaint law-enforcement way, but I was in no mood then to appreciate the subtleties of his wit.

'I was only using it to stuff my shoulder with,' I cried in a strangulated voice, throwing all vestiges of pride and self-respect to the winds in a wild effort to clear my name.

'To do what?' he ejaculated.

'To stuff my shoulders. This coat was too big for me so I stuffed these newspapers in the shoulders to make it fit better.'

'And then to make it fit worse you took them out again and stuffed them in your pants pockets ! Did that make your trousers fit better ?'

He looked at my burlesque garb with profound mistrust : I could almost feel the handcuffs on my wrists.

'Look,' I cried, 'I don't know what has happened to my invitation, but see that young lady over there ? She is with me. She'll tell you I had one.'

The FBI man grabbed my arm and led me across to my date, whose eyes opened with wonder as we approached.

'This guy with you ?' he asked.

'Yes,' she replied, 'that is, in so far as he is with anyone. He seems a bit out of this world tonight.'

'Got an invite ?' he asked, letting go of my arm.

'Certainly. Look, one for me and one for him.' She opened her bag and produced her invitation—mine, too. I remembered then that I had given it to her for safe keeping, since I am always losing that sort of thing.

The man looked at them carefully. 'O.K.,' he said, with an almost reluctant sigh. 'They look all right. But you'd better keep an eye on your friend. If I find him climbing up on the President's Box again he'll land up in the hoosgow, no matter how many invitations he has. And if you'll pardon my saying so,' he added, turning to me, 'if I were you I'd put those you-know-whats back in your coat. It needs them.'

My date gave me a look that might be described as almost respectful as we walked back to our table. 'What on earth were you doing ?' she asked.

'Oh, nothing,' I replied listlessly, the taste of defeat bitter in my mouth. 'I was just trying to see the President when that guard came along and nabbed me.'

'But why ?'

'I was climbing up on the stand. I suppose he thought I was a crank or something.'

'I expect he probably did. Now look here. You don't have to behave like a kid and climb up poles in order to see the President. All you have to do is to wait until the show is over and then go to the edge of the dance floor. He'll walk right by you, and there won't be anyone in front to block your view.'

I recognized the soundness of her plan. We watched the rest of the show in silence. As soon as it was over, we pushed our way to the front of the audience and waited for the President to come by.

The band played the National Anthem and then broke into the strains of 'So Long, Chief,' or whatever the name of the tune is which they play when the President is leaving places. There was a stir in the Presidential Box as everyone prepared to leave. Had I been nearer the box, I might have caught a glimpse of Mr Truman as he descended the stairs. As it was, he was hidden from my view the whole time. As soon as he reached the floor he was, moreover, immediately lost in the crowd. Nevertheless I stood my ground, for I knew that in order to leave he had to come our way, and would pass within a few feet of me. At last victory was to be mine. I was going to see the President. I only hoped he would be worth all I had gone through. He had certainly put me to a lot of trouble.

That set me thinking. It was obviously worth a lot of discomfort to see the President. People often travelled hundreds of miles and stayed all night just to catch a glimpse of him. But millions of people *had* seen the President, and millions more *would*. Thousands of people, moreover, had been invited to Presidential receptions ; and Mr Truman would be seen by thousands more at similar functions before his term of office expired. Why, there must be at least a thousand people there that evening. They had all seen President Truman. Everyone in the ballroom must have seen him in fact—except me. And now *I* was about to see him. A wave of handclapping and the click of shoes on parquet flooring announced this as a certainty. I was about to see the President. I was about to be just like everyone else. I was *what* ?

I closed my eyes and kept them tight shut until I knew the President had passed by.

Yes, I am the only man in history who has gone to a Presidential Reception and refused to see the President. It is, I am sure you must agree, a unique distinction.

THE LIFE AND DEATH OF

PIERROT

by KAY DICK

T O UNDERSTAND him properly it is essential to know something about his family, because Pierrot was not suddenly created an entity unto himself. Indeed, as we study him more closely, it becomes clear that Pierrot has always been very much part of the family, environment and tradition he inherited. From the early days of his long apprenticeship of the sixteenth and seventeenth centuries, throughout his years of fame during the eighteenth and nineteenth centuries, to the paradoxical tragedy of his decline in the twentieth century, Pierrot leaves no one in doubt about his kinship with that great European family of travelling comedians whose dynasty reached its zenith with the Italian branch known as the *Commedia dell' Arte.*

Although a son of that illustrious household, Pierrot experienced a continuous, often bitter struggle to obtain his birthright. At first barely acknowledged, almost illegitimate, he progressed in obscurity while his kinsmen consolidated their claims in fierce and open competition. Neglected, ill-used, abused, he endured and survived poverty, servitude, humiliation, and misinterpretation, to emerge at last, from being a pitiable scapegoat, as the rightful heir of a family whose history so dramatically portrays the European humanities.

Like all families with ancient pride, the Comedians boasted of links with classical Greece and Rome. There is much talk of antiquity in their genealogy, with especial reference to the plays of Terentus from Carthage, of Plautus from Umbria, of the *Atellenae* fables of the Roman Campagna. An understandable tribal vanity when it is recalled that Atella was the first Roman city to have a theatre—an associative claim which denotes a sense of property, strong in a family whose material circumstances were mostly those of eviction. This claim to such distinguished ancestry is reasonably valid because many of the *Atellanae* characters were precursors of *Commedia dell' Arte* personalities, and their scenarios—comedies, parodies, political satires—had in common the fact that whatever the argument the rôles kept the same characters. Furthermore all *Atellanae* players wore masks, a fashion imitated by most of the Comedians until the eighteenth century. The *Atellanae* were the opposition to written drama : improvisation and mime illustrated and expanded their bare plots. These classical ancestors stressed what Pierrot was to perfect, the importance of individuality and personal freedom in terms of human experience : '*la nécéssité de sentir et de créer à soi seul son personnage.*' No *Commedia dell' Arte* character found it harder to retain his individuality ; none more constantly battled to achieve personal freedom. Pierrot's progress was a long and lonely pilgrimage from the establishment of an identity to emancipation and fulfilment as an active creative artist.

In the beginning Pierrot was overshadowed by the more vociferous members of his family, all desperately intent on the building-up of their dynasty. Chroniclers, historians, and illustrators offer innumerable facts and legends, often contradictory, when they describe the pioneer days of those acrobats, tight-rope dancers and tumblers who travelled to and fro across Europe. Whereas the detail of nomenclature differs there is agreement about the manner and method of the art which these vagabonds practised and perfected. Creators of popular theatre, their improvisations, based on direct observation, were concerned with drama and comedy which all could understand. They introduced themselves as immediately recognizable characters, whereas the popular actors of the legitimate theatre were always identifiable apart from the characters they depicted. As the Comedians moved from one country to another, the language barrier was overcome by the use of mime. According to the pictorial record of Callot's *I Balli di Sfessania* (*Petits Danseurs*) drawings, Pierrot's family were a grotesque lot as they caroused their way through Europe with their wives, children and performing animals. In Fricasso's torn garments and simplicity in battle (he mostly turned his back on his enemy) there is a glimpse of Pierrot the pacifist. Chased from one district to another, dependent on the favour of clergy or sovereign, the Comedians developed, as do the refugees, a necessary sense of communal solidarity. Handed down from generation to generation was the craft of their art, an art constantly revitalized as new qualities were infused, inherited, added to, until, at the beginning of the sixteenth century, they came forward in all their pride as the Italian players of the *Commedia dell' Arte*.

Scaramucia. Fricasso.

Engraving by Callot (British Museum)

Where was Pierrot during these evolutionary years ? In the comedies of Plautus and Terentus he is to be found in the Slave, early identifying himself with the outcast. The *sunnio* (*buffon*) of the *Atellanae*, he was the zany of all work, the youngest son of those travelling pioneers, employed mostly to attract the crowd to the performance of his elders and betters. Occasionally he was the stand-in, the unwilling understudy, which accounts for much biographical confusion. Some Harlequins bear traces of Pierrot, as does the famous Meissen Harlequin of Kändler ; and many Pulchinellas conceal a Pedrolino, visual evidence which links with similar transmogrifications in the scenarios.

Bohemians borrow the modes and manners of countries they temporarily adopt, and all *Commedia dell' Arte* personalities altered their fashions according to the customs of the lands through which they made their way. These variations explain the contradictions of chroniclers, although at the beginning of the sixteenth century the main *Commedia dell' Arte* characters became more or less fixed.

To know Pierrot one must know about those whose lives he shared, because his eventual emancipation came from a continuous protest against the values of his kinsmen ; in fact his silent rebellion was against the family's materialism, greed, opportunism and accommodating morality, which ultimately he rejected.

Ruling and bullying the clan were the Doctor and Pantaloon, two old men linked by strategic alliance rather than natural friendship. The unworldly, self-styled, erudite Doctor claimed the University city of Bologna as his academic Mecca. Representing the cultural 'establishment,' his was the accepted word on all matters of learning, although his judgement and behaviour showed him to have lacked understanding of those arts associated with his honorary degrees. More final an authority was Pantaloon, of Venetian origin, whose name (Plant-the-lion) symbolizes 'increase your wealth,' and accounts for his being both a rich tradesman and a miser. This material power enabled him to play the rôle of elder Statesman. Although the Doctor could and did pontificate at every turn, it was Pantaloon who controlled the exchequer. Also part of this upper-crust were the Captain (Scaramouche) and Pulchinella (eventually to become the English Punch and the French Polichinelle). Like Pantaloon, whose business associate he was, the Captain originated from Venice, city of adventurers and sea merchants. An out-and-out militarist, he was mercenary by instinct, a bully by nature, an oppressor of the people, an unscrupulous womanizer, an anti-romantic with a nose for the main chance. Unlike Pantaloon, the Captain had no taste for civic honours, and was therefore better able to ignore decencies of behaviour, considering himself to be above ethics. Naples gave a final identity to Pulchinella, who served both Pantaloon and the Doctor. His was a dual character : he had two fathers, one very noble, the other of lowly birth, consequently he was better able than most to come quickly to the aid of the party in power. Eccentric, witty, bestial, self-centred and cruel, he was in turn magistrate, poet, schoolmaster and spy. It was not until the middle of the seventeenth century that he created his own ministry as Punch, King of the Marionettes.

Employed by Pantaloon and the Doctor, oppressed and tormented by the Captain and Pulchinella, were the valets, a hierarchy below-stairs, tyrannized over by Harlequin from Bergamo, a city whose people were reputed to be slow-witted, sly and knavish. The lackey of merchants, thieves and panderers, Harlequin learned his many tricks from his masters, assuming with ease virtues and vices to fit the moment, ever careful to be available at the division of any spoils. His artful resilence was illustrated in the blue, red and green diamond lozenges (originally triangles) of his dress, which suggests a triple-edged allegiance. His double-pointed cap indicated a trace of Negro blood, which makes a genealogical link with the plays of the

Engraving by Callot (British Museum)

Carthaginian Terentus. It is only fair to point out that in the seventeenth century Harlequin, under the player Domenico Biancolelli's tutelage, acquired a certain refinement of manners, some intelligence, a sharper wit and much elegance, although he still remained incurably mischievous. Like Pantaloon, whose household he supervised, Harlequin employed his own Captain, one Brighella from his home town, an arch-intriguer, a swaggering, offensive and brutish rogue, whose addiction to the costly pleasures of drink, women and gambling forced him to serve those who also serve. A natural aptitude for singing and playing the guitar brought Brighella temporary notoriety as Flautino, as Mezzetino.

A host of other retainers and menials jostled each other in the battle for survival, devoting what leisure they could secure to win favours from the *soubrettes*, whose reigning queen was Columbine from Naples, sometimes introduced as Francischina from Tuscany, a lady who could seldom resist the muscular poetry of Harlequin's physical grace, which made her forgive him his many infidelities. This same Columbine–Francischina was the romantic love of Pierrot's life and death.

Columbine–Francischina was courted by all the leading male *Commedia dell' Arte* characters, and married to most of them in turn, even to the Doctor and to Pantaloon, the old men, though sometimes she was introduced as the daughter or niece of one of them. Whereas the constancy of the others fluc-tuated according to circumstances, there was never any wavering in Pierrot's devoted loyalty to Colum-bine, whatever name she or he assumed. Less successful than others in his courtship, Pierrot did, occasionally, enjoy the privilege and pleasure of being her hus-band ; this most often when Columbine called herself Francis-china. On the whole Pierrot's love-behaviour was fraught with Proustian complications, especially when Harlequin decided to bid at the same time. When Francis-china deceived him, Pierrot wept tears of self-reproach, judging him-self to be the guilty party, accept-ing her deceit as an indication of some failure in himself. When Columbine deceived Harlequin with the Captain or Brighella, Pierrot intrigued and plotted until he had brought her back to Harlequin's arms. The love-relationship of these three retained a constant sexual ambivalence, a sort of gang behaviour of three in love with love, allowing no outsider any permanent conquest of Columbine's heart. Pierrot knew that he would, and often did, lose Columbine to Harlequin, yet in this loss there was no loss of his love, because Columbine's love for Harlequin, which was part of her, became an intrinsic part of Pierrot's love for Columbine, if only because he was dedicated to love everything about her.

Such was the company Pierrot kept. His standing as a valet was lower than Harlequin's. He was most often employed by the Doctor, although in fact he acquired an initial identity as Pierro, when he was attached, in 1547, to Pantaloon. A complicated character, even at this stage, he was unique among valets for being extremely honest. His weakness was a tendency to fall asleep while watching over his master's wife or daughter, and he aped insanity in order to escape the consequent blows. He dressed in a white nightshirt, wore a pointed straw hat, and carried a wooden stick. He was absent-minded, and apt to lose letters which were entrusted to him.

The chronology of Pierrot's apprenticeship fans out like a man stretched on the wheel, and indeed the poignant history of these years records a perpetual investigation into the identity of one forced to assume many names and many natures, until such time as he could openly proclaim himself.

As Bertoldo, the peasant from Verona, with the round head, flat red hair, big ears, small eyes, thick, bulbous nose, slack mouth stretching across his face, teeth like a boar's, bowlegged, even so he acquired a reputation for sound judgement, pleasant and agreeable manners, ability as a speaker and wisdom as an arbitrator. As Bertoldino, he impressed the King of Verona with his paradoxical and practical humour. His worst habit was a long melancholic complaint about life, which he accompanied himself on a stringed instrument.

As Pedrolino, a mixture of naïvety and rustic craftiness, he was known for his agility as a dancer and his skill as a hunter, especially successful with game ; and thus he enjoyed some popularity. As the 1570 Pagliaccio, dismissed as a *Paillasse,** juggler and acrobat, he was scorned as a mere sideshow barker, his simplicity debased to vulgarity, his native air of wonder taken for idiocy. In 1598, he introduced himself as Gian-Farina (Jean-Farine). His face plastered with coarse flour which stressed his grimace, he dressed in an outsize crumpled shift, and sported a wooden sword. A flexible white hat, which could be manipulated into any shape, was sometimes replaced by a pointed cap. He appeared to be stupid, clumsy, slow-witted, an avowed coward who yet continually took the less cautious action, especially when related to physical prowess, which usually resulted in his dragging down the master he affected to support. In Gian-Farina, Pierrot anticipated his decline into the English Clown. Towards the

The poorest and most wretched of clowns.

GILLES *by Jean Antoine Watteau (Paris, Louvre)*

On the left is a Bow porcelain Pierrot, 1760. Below it is a Pierrot with postillion whip, made by Klösterveil, 1770. Both are in the Victoria and Albert Museum

Above is a Meissen figure of Harlequin, modelled by Kändler in 1740 (British Museum). On the page opposite is Renoir's painting of his son Coco in Pierrot costume (Copyright, s.p.a.d.e.m.)

LA PRÉSENTATION *by Gavarni (detail)*

end of the sixteenth century this Gian-Farina made his appearance as the Burgundian Gros-Guillaume, a fat baker who wore two belts, dispensed with his mask, and enjoyed some favour as a joker, being praised by Henri IV and Richelieu. In Sicily he dressed in light blue, ceased to powder his face, and was known as Peppe-Nappa, a wonderful dancer and acrobat, said to be boneless, whose greatest vice was gluttony. As Giglio, towards the end of the sixteenth century, he tripped forward as the amorous valet dressed in white flannel. In 1670 as Zanieri, he presented himself as the Neapolitan Pulchinella and the Gilles he was to become in the eighteenth century.

Certain definite and important aspects of the fundamental Pierrot revealed themselves during this apprenticeship. Working mostly for the Doctor, the guardian of knowledge, Pierrot showed himself to be a lover of the arts. Early he questioned the power of the sword over the pen, which explains why he was in perpetual conflict with Pantaloon's household and Harlequin's tyranny, a combination of power established mainly through the Captain's brute force and Brighella's ruffianism. Furthermore, Pierrot was the only one who dared to question the validity of the Doctor's pronouncements, simply because he was the one on whom fell all the initial work of research. At night, while the Doctor slept, Pierrot probed and enquired into the true nature of the moon, working until his candle burnt out and he had no strength left to light another.

This passion for truth is shown in the variety of selves through which Pierrot revealed his fundamental self. While his kinsmen were content to remain as they were, their development never progressing beyond the aggrandizement of the accepted self, Pierrot always sought new areas of personal experience, often when this necessitated giving up benefits gained. A poet among materialists and men of action, he was often accused of cowardice because he failed to take the main chance. His retreats were victories rather than defeats, enabling him to begin all over again to explore the matter from some previously undiscovered channel. He provoked no enmity because his inherent good nature was interpreted as simple-mindedness. He revealed himself slowly in stages, ever careful not to usurp another's dominion, desiring nothing but the true expression of himself at the right time in the proper place.

Even so, working as he did underground, statistics from the scenarios show Pierrot's performance to be greater than Harlequin's, because out of a total of 275 family archives of this period, Pedrolino appears in

52 to Harlequin's 43. Thus, almost by stealth, did Pierrot come into his birthright. In 1665, for the first time, he introduced himself as Pierrot, the hero of a divertissement, *Don Juan ou le Festin de Pierre*, presented by Molière in *Le Misanthrope* at the Théâtre Français in Paris. Dressed in a white suit with a large collar and a black hat, this Pierrot, hero at last, credulous and sceptical, with dreams of love, inspired La Bruyère to write his famous chapter on the European peasant. All recognized this Pierrot as '*le peuple*.' It was the landmark to the years of fame.

The Comedians crossed from Italy into France during the reign of Charles IX, and on the invitation of Catherine de' Medici were installed at the Palais Royal theatre in the centre of Paris. Forced to leave because of the jealousy of the resident company, the Confrèrerie de la Passion, who claimed to be founders of the French theatre, the Comedians returned again under Henri III, but Parliament, treating them as a refugee problem, got rid of them. Returning yet again, they enjoyed the court's favour until 1697

Peppe-Nappa, 1770, by Maurice Sand

when, for offending the prudish Madame de Maintenon, they were banished for nineteen years to reside thirty leagues outside the capital.

By now Pierrot was walking abroad under his real name, and although he and his family were temporarily limited to the fairgrounds outside Paris, hobnobbing once again with the riff-raff and the tooth-extractors, they had tasted the glory of almost becoming legitimate theatre. This first flavour of splendour was to prove a dangerous drug, because when the family returned in 1716, during the reign of Louis XV, brought back from exile in triumph to the Palais Royal by the Regent as an antidote to the prevailing gloom, this second feast of fortune went to their heads.

They came under the protection of the Duchesse de Berry, were granted a royal subsidy in 1723, and installed at the residence of their former rivals, at the Hôtel de Bourgogne, as the Comediens Ordinaires du Roi. Material success had also come, in some measure, to Pierrot by way of a song, composed in 1712 by Hamoche, one of his earliest *impresarios*, *Au Clair de la Lune*—a song which could belong to no other member of the family, a song whose reference to burnt-out candles and Pierrot's right to the pen held memories of the long apprenticeship at night, behind bolted doors in the Doctor's laboratory at Bologna.

> Au clair de la lune
> Mon ami Pierrot,
> Prêtes-moi ta plume
> Pour ècrire un mot.
> Ma chandelle est morte
> Je n'ai plus de feu,
> Ouvre-moi ta porte
> Pour l'amour de Dieu.

Towards the middle of the eighteenth century it seemed as though the motto implied in Pantaloon's name, 'increase your wealth,' inspired the whole family. Rich and powerful, fêted and respected, the Comedians opened their own theatre, Le Théâtre des Italiens. Even Pierrot basked in this wave of popularity. Fashionable painters competed to capture his likeness, with Watteau in the lead, introducing him as

Pagliaccio, 1600, by Maurice Sand

Gilles, the darling of the aristocratic masked balls, the silken-clad, lace-ruffed zany of smart picnic parties. There are rumours that Pierrot sometimes tired of this life of ease, because one hears of his occasional appearances in Italy, in Austria, with kinsmen who never left the road. There is gossip of him as Petrouchka with the Marionettes, further evidence of his boredom with the *débutantes* and their frivolities.

This surfeit of luxury and wealth carried its own poison of deterioration ; the family's art declined as their material success increased. The craft of improvisation gave way to the pride and pomp of being legitimate theatre, with excursions into opera, ballet, plays, until the spoken word became more important than mime. Apeing their patrons, the Comedians over-reached themselves. Even Pierrot grew fat, which is as tragic as saying that Pierrot almost ceased to be. The true Pierrot belongs to those who may not be able to eat tomorrow. Thus, these first years of fame were only in fact years of plenty. It took a revolution and a Napoleon Bonaparte to lead Pierrot and what remained of his kinsmen to their real years of fame.

Patronless once again, in the early nineteenth century, Pierrot and the remnants of his family (many had abdicated to the rich) were back in the pit of humanity, ever their natural habitat, in this case Paris, in the Boulevard du Temple, popularly known as the Boulevard du Crime, taking their turn on the boards of the Petit Théâtre des Funambules, seating 780. Here in the shoddiness of the second-hand markets, in the wasteland of the dispossessed and the petty crooks, Pierrot, who had almost lost his true identity as Gilles sucking up to the rich, found the fullness of his art. He ambled through the sweaty crowds, holes in his shoes, eating stale potato chips, drinking cheap red wine, reverting to the use of common flour for his face, because no longer could he afford the expensive theatrical grease paint which had made him such a tame gallant in the years of plenty. Here at last, in poverty again, Pierrot became art.

At the Funambules, introduced by Gaspard Deburau, his greatest *impresario*,* Pierrot re-lived the stages of his life—his evolutionary years, the long apprenticeship, the sudden fame. Working at first as a stage-hand Paillasse to Mr and Mrs Godot, the first Funambulists, whose drunken human pyramid act Pierrot had to support, often to his disadvantage, he graduated through every dirty costume, the most humiliating chores, mocked by the locals as a half-witted crank,

* Throughout I have used *impresario* to refer to various actors, players, dancers, painters, etc., who have created a version of Pierrot which has become universally accepted.

A Fool, by Marcellus Laroon (British Museum)

kicked and beaten as he went about his dreary round of barking, scene-shifting, carpentry, submitting to the indignities of his Godot masters, suffering as he presented the degrading spectacle of the *chiens savants*, driven to attempt suicide. During the Hundred Days a chance encounter with the Emperor Napoleon, before whose carriage Pierrot, drunk and half-starved, collapsed, provided him with his final inspiration. Napoleon invited him to explain his art—the all-embracing human art of the anonymous *Paillasse*. The prestige of this interview, when it became known, made Pierrot a star overnight.

For fifteen years, with the devoted and dedicated Deburau behind him, Pierrot showed his full face to the world, that real and true face of Pierrot which only the moon so far had known intimately. There in the most squalid quarter of Paris, Pierrot created the glory of his art, a perfection of personality which drew all worlds to meet at the little Funambules theatre. Jules Janin, the 'prince' of critics, came and came again, and wrote about the genius of this luminous Pierrot. Authors such as George Sand, Victor Hugo, Alfred de Musset, Théophile Gautier, de Banville and Béranger added their golden words. Actresses as celebrated as the Mlles Mars and Georges and Madame Malibran sat entranced by the vital theatrical face which went beyond the stage. Painters such as Gérard, playwrights such as Picard, all came to learn and wonder, and Redouté, the man of the roses, was one of those who watched this Pierrot with a rose. Society ladies dreamt about him, middle-class housewives wished their husbands were more like him, young men adopted his graces, and the local tradesmen of the Boulevard du Crime bowed as he passed their stalls, offering him their choicest delicacies. For the first time some were jealous of him, an envy which is the strongest evidence of Pierrot's triumph, because no one previously had bothered to view him as a possible rival. This may account for the revenge taken by the twentieth century.

Pedrolino, 1673, by Maurice Sand

It was *l'Amour* and *la Gloire* simultaneously, which Pierrot had sought all his life. He had a visiting-card—*Artiste, Funambulist, Mime.* Something no one throughout the centuries had thought of offering him was offered—a contract, a three-year contract (dated 1828–31) with a guaranteed 35 francs per week—a sum Pierrot used to acquire what he had never owned, property. Two hundred and sixty-six objects, all related to his art. A selection from this property offers an illuminating glimpse into Pierrot's world : a steel watch chain, a silver bell, a desk, a magician's wand, a flute, many books, some laurel flowers, a leather writing-case, a basket of fruit, a small drinking flask, a lantern, a *bonbonnière*, three scarves, a black cat, a peacock, a *legion d'honneur* medal, a box of rain, a golden key, a looking-glass, a streak of lightning, a ladder, a pipe, a game of loto, a bunch of red roses, a pistol, ten bank notes, a coffin, a fan, a guitar, half a sheet, a bag of nails, a compass, a crucifix, a sponge, some gambling counters, four boxes of dragees, scissors, a cage containing an impaled bird, a pumpkin, a first-aid kit, a pair of candlesticks, a bottle of maras-

Pierrot, 1846, by Maurice Sand

chino, a plate of biscuits, a postillion whip, a gold topped walking-stick, a billiard cue, a green umbrella, a painted wooden harp, an artist's palette, a set of geometrical instruments, a dagger, a hunting horn, a skull, a book of law.

From the *chiens savants* he selected his own little bitch, one Coquette, a miniature dog who was never far from him. He had a love (yes, that same love) to whom daily he brought small gifts such as a sugar dog, a bunch of parma violets, a small glass of chocolate liqueur. Rich though he was in his world, he refused to pay for a carriage to send his love home in the rain and gave her his green umbrella instead.

What did he look like, this Pierrot ? He was tall and thin and haggard with thinking ; he wore his immaculate white linen suit with a casual loose elegance, dispensing with the collar of his servitude, showing his bare and vulnerable throat to his enemies. Thrown away was the straw hat of the village idiot, the fool's pointed cap, the courtier's satin head-dress ; instead he wore with rightful pride the velvet skull cap of the scholar. Serious, intense, ironic, pensive was his expression. A paradox of what was and what is not, he was the people and the poet, in turn gay, sad, ill, exuberant, triumphant, melancholic, soaked with and desolated by knowledge. Ever gracious and tender, even in adversity, and he rarely lived far from adversity, his instinct was that of experience understood. He knew what made the people laugh, what made them angry, what they anticipated, what they feared, what they loved. He knew why men beat their wives, got drunk, were tender and cruel with their children, how they contracted debts, married off their daughters and how they died. Certain places pleased him especially—small hotels, taverns, attics, gambling dens, woods, open-air spectacles, cafés, all inexpensive places of entertainment where the common man and the artist met. He looked and became what he saw, as he worked to express the human experience of life and death, his indecisive aspect contradicted by the sad tightness of his mocking mouth. Nothing astonished him ; his patience with mankind was inexhaustible. He was, as Janin wrote, *'chaste et original, dans un monde usé il a été neuf.'*

Hardly using the spoken word, casting it aside as irrelevant, mischievous and untrue, Pierrot was summed up by his *impresario* Deburau in the epitaph: 'Ci-git un comedien qui a tout dit et qui n'a jamais parlé.'

Death has ever been part of Pierrot's experience, and in life he was to know this darkness, as art is familiar with corruption. Following the death of Charles Deburau, Gaspard's son, Pierrot began to drift. It seemed as though, stricken with grief, he lost a measure of his breathing. Friends and minor funambulists there still were to help and lessen the burden of his decline. *Impresarios* like Paul Legrand, who had taken Pierrot as far as Rio de Janiero, in 1863, persuaded him to tour, but it was a lesser Pierrot who made his bow, although many found him more amiable, because there was less mockery in his investigation of human frailty.

PIERROT *by Pablo Picasso*, 1918 (*New York, Museum of Modern Art*)

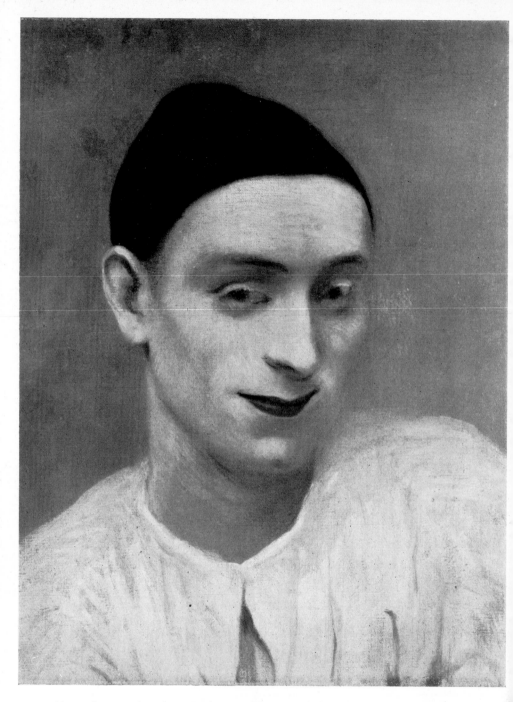

Above is reproduced an Unknown Pierrot, *c.* 1890, by an unknown artist (Coll. Miss Kathleen Farrell)—a typical Deburau Pierrot, as perfected by Charles, the son. At the top of the opposite page is a Baron photograph of the John Cranko ballet, *Harlequin in April*. Below, on the left, is Marcel Marceau in *Pantomimes* (Films de France); on the right is Jean-Louis Barrault in *Les Enfants du Paradis* (British Film Institute)

THE WISE PIERROT *by Georges Rouault, 1945 (New York, Mr and Mrs Alex L. Hillm*

In 1883, a great professional tribute was paid to Pierrot by no less distinguished a celebrity than Madame Sarah Bernhardt, when she gave her interpretation of Pierrot at the Palais du Trocadero in a sketch, *Pierrot Assassin*, by Jean Richepin.

But the twentieth century found Pierrot ambling, almost aimlessly, between the worlds of the fast disappearing funambulists and the new Bohemians who attempted, without much success, to establish themselves in the fashionable Champs Elysées at little *café-spectacles* which sprang up and vanished overnight.

At the beginning of this century it was as though Pierrot were suffering from some mysterious sickness—*un malaise* the French called it. He appeared unable to return to his true identity ; one almost suspects him of suicidal tendencies as we read of his joining the marionettes and the vaudeville performers. Moving from the Champs Elysées into Montmartre, Pierrot, through a new *impresario*, the strip-cartoon artist Adolphe Wilette, strutted about as an indigent artist, an *habitué* of the Moulin Rouge, a macabre and pessimistic frequenter of sordid carbarets like Le Chat Noir, a reader of Schopenhauer whose talk was of despair as he prowled about the Moulin de la Galette. Taken up by Huysman as Pierrot Sceptique, he dressed in black and mourned for the death of his love. The novelist Paul Marguerite described Pierrot returning from the cemetery where they had buried Columbine, a Pierrot drunk, remorseful, riddled with nightmares, convinced he had killed her, constantly haunted.

Some echoes of his greater glories came back through poetry ; Théophile Gautier, Baudelaire, Apollinaire were among those who recognized him to be the art they struggled to preserve. Verlaine, inspired by him, proclaimed his paradoxical immortality : *C'est le Sage, c'est le Fou, c'est l'enfant gâté de la lune.* Impressionist painters— Degas, Lautrec, Saurat, le Douanier Rousseau—saw lights in his face which illuminated aspects of their new art, although most of them introduced him by his English name, Clown.

Pierrot, corrupted by England, had been debased to Clown. Grimaldi and his disciples had launched the caricature ; a savage travesty of the Funambule Pierrot, cheeks padded and reddened, long thin mouth stretched from ear to ear and thickened with scarlet paint, slender height beaten down into a shapeless ungainly lump, immaculate white suit star-sprung and spattered with clashing-coloured ribbons, neat velvet scholar's cap replaced by the fool's pointed cone hung with bells. Pierrot's mime was perverted to coarse gestures, his voice, used of late only for singing, trained to a cacophony of neighing laughter. Clown was Pierrot's decline, a barbarous and cruel impersonation, provoking merriment instead of wonder.

At the beginning of the twentieth century it looked as though Clown had exterminated Pierrot, as though the caricature were the reality. Clown is in fact a deliberate concealment of Pierrot, and there is fear in the laughter which this undignified status provokes.

Pierrot has not entirely disappeared. Many are the references to his true self and the variety of his human experience in this twentieth century. In music and in the ballet he is to be found, particularly through the choreographer Fokine, who allowed him to come through as the nineteenth century Pierrot, dressed by Bakst, in *Le Carnival*, 1910. Nijinsky, although presenting him as the puppet Petrouchka in 1911, unveiled his true face to the world again. In the unrealities of pantomime, however, it is as Clown that Pierrot made and still makes his protest. As Clown also did the modern painters first become aware of him—the clown of the Cirque Medrano, where, before the first world war, artists with new visions like Picasso and Juan Gris first encountered him.

In England he toured as Pierrot, a Pierrot without identity, a Pierrot even without his caricature of Clown, a Pierrot dressed as any summer holiday stroller with a boater and a cane walking-stick, who sang on the sands. No more pitiable illustration of this Pierrot of the piers can be found than in Walter Sickert's *Brighton Pierrots*.

Grimaldi as Clown, in 'Mother Goose'

[226]

Even so, men with new dimensions in their minds like Severini, Dufy, Brancusi and others were simultaneously rediscovering the real Pierrot, and it is enlightening to trace the impact of Pierrot on the work of two of the greatest modern European painters, Picasso and Roualt. Through Picasso the communist and Roualt the Catholic, Pierrot has managed to survive the corruption of Clown.

Before he was twenty-five Picasso illustrated some part of the true perspective of the European Pierrot through the tragic realities and anguish of his Blue Period paintings which produced the Rose Period of the *Saltimbiques*. Picasso's *cirque forain* sums up the sickness of the twentieth century ; these grave and dispossessed kinsmen of Pierrot

Vaslav Nijinsky as Petrouchka
Photograph by Elliot & Fry

are a prophecy of the refugees of the 'thirties, the war-victims of the 'forties, the displaced persons of the 'fifties. Picasso knows that Pierrot is *le peuple* and, like Deburau, he understands him to be the introspective enquiring mind of man, fighting on the last barricade against the growing forces of power-politics and tyranny. Like Pierrot himself, Picasso, whose work has progressed through startling changes from decade to decade, understands the experience of identity lost and regained of *l'homme engagé* : 'What do you think an artist is ? An imbecile who has only his eyes if he is a painter, or his ears if a musician, or a lyre at every level of his heart-throbs, if he is a poet, or—even if he is only a boxer—just his muscles ? On the contrary, he is at the same time a political being, constantly alert to the heart-rending, burning, or happy events in the world, moulding himself in their likeness.' Picasso has never forgotten Pierrot or his family ; his great cubist paintings of 1923 introduced yet again these *Commedia dell' Arte* personalities. What they stand for in human terms is constantly expressed, again and again in new shapes, in Picasso's art.

[227]

Whereas Pierrot, through Picasso's work, assumes, as he did in his own life, many identities, in the work of the Catholic painter Roualt he is entirely a being of the twentieth century, coming to us with the duality this century has forced on him : Pierrot–Clown. Roualt understood the co-existence of caricature and reality, the paradox of human experience which enables a man to be simultaneously himself and a monster of himself.

Roualt's personal awareness of Pierrot began in 1903, when he was thirty-two. He had seen Pierrot before, through Forain, Daumier and Lautrec, but in that all-important year of 1903, Roualt came to his discovery of Pierrot in the way of a man temporarily blind suddenly regaining sight. 'I saw what I had seen before, but the form of it, and the harmony, were new.' Roualt was, he stated, shaken to the roots of his creative being. 'One day I noticed how, when a beautiful day turns to evening, the first star shines out in the sky. It moved me deeply—I don't know why—and it marked the beginnings of poetry in my life. A gypsy caravan halted at the side of the road, a weary old horse nibbling stunted grasses, an old clown patching his costume— the contrast, in fact, between the brilliance and scintillation of laughter and the intense sadness of life itself . . . That was how it began. Then I enlarged it all. I saw quite clearly that the clown was myself, us, all of us, almost . . . The gaudy spangled dress was what life gives us. We all wear a spangled dress of some sort, but if someone catches us with the spangles off, as I caught that old clown, oh ! the infinite pity of it !'

Thenceforth Roualt's art was re-dedicated, inspired by that original personal vision of Pierrot glimpsed through Clown : 'Anyone who bases his entire art on one glance from a broken-down acrobat must be crazed with pride—or entirely humble, if that's the purpose he was made for.' And, during all the fifty-four years which remained to him, Roualt never went back on his basic inspiration : his first self-portrait was in the guise of a Pierrot, and he explored Clown until he found the Pierrot he knew was there.

Today he is still with us, this Pierrot unknown, whose life and death express the whole range of the creative artist, whose knowledge is experience, whose experience belongs to the next man, whose dispossession is immortality, because his art is concerned with the communication of human experience—identity lost and identity regained.

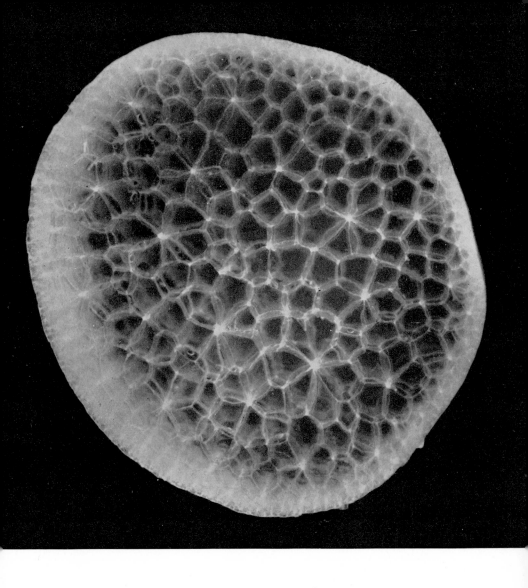

MAGNIFICATIONS

Micro-photographs by DOUGLAS F. LAWSON *and* E. O. HOPPÉ

The object shown above is the least of the magnifications shown in the ensuing pages. It is only about twice natural size, but takes on a strange and beautiful air as a result of light being projected through it, as in an X-ray picture. The object—a water hyacinth.

Above : Sodium Azide crystals, 50 times magnified. *Below :* Wing scales of a butte

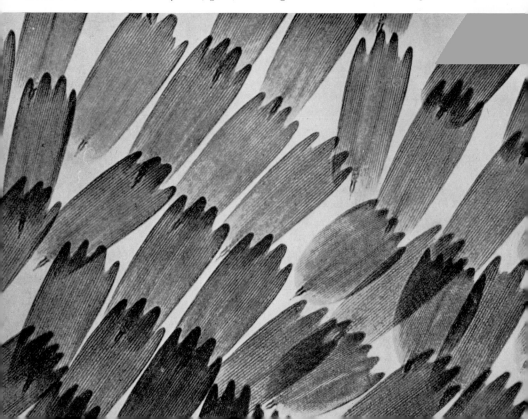

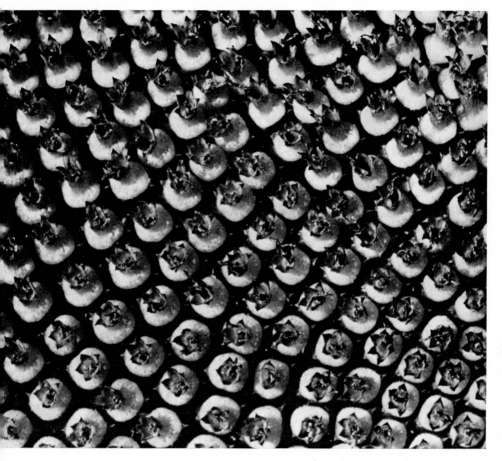

Above : a section of a sunflower seed

Eggs of a house-fly

Skin of a sole

Above : Eggs of Large White Cabbage butterfly, 100 times magnified
Below : Needle of a Scotch Fir

Mono-cyclohixylamine crystals, 150 times magnified

A baked potato

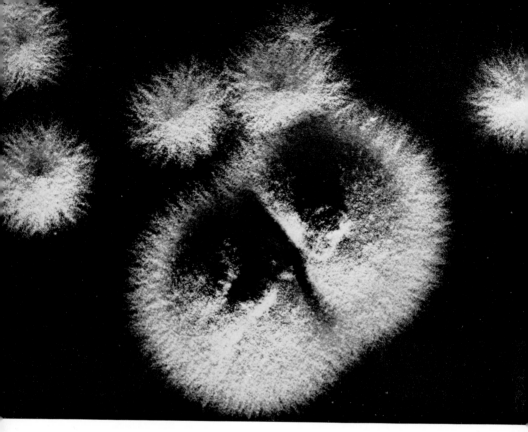

Penicillium glaucum mould, 25 times magnified

Ving scales of Painted Lady butterfly,
70 times magnified

Wing scales of Emperor moth, 80 times
magnified

THE ART OF THE WALL

Parisian graffiti *photographed and discussed by* B R A S S A I

WHY SHOULD it be that in an age dominated, as ours is, by the exact sciences, there is so tremendous an interest taken in primitive art, be it stone or iron age, prehellenic or Mexican, Peruvian or Asiatic ? Why are we more excited by the beginnings of art than by masterpieces produced in the great ages ? The reason is that the earliest impulses in art seem to spring up from a deeper stratum, from a purer source, which seem better able to illuminate for us the fact of artistic creation which so preoccupies us today. We are always hoping to discern beneath the carved or painted figures of primitive art the true being of man, the essence of the human spirit.

Apart from the Primitives, the madmen and the *naifs*—those who have lost their reason or who have not yet acquired it—it is children who enable us to participate most closely in the birth of art. The early years of a human being are perhaps not unlike the early stages of the human race. With its heroes, monsters, myths and legends, childhood has something of the candour and innocence, the strange and disturbing quality, of the world of early man. Psychologists have in all seriousness attempted to mark off each of the 'periods' of child-artists, from their prehistoric scribblings to their classic phase of patterns and symbols, down to the age of narrative and finally to the decline which sets in at the age of ten when the child's fragile creative gift usually fades for ever.

Children's drawings and paintings are in fashion, and are now even to be found in museums ; but there remains another branch of child-creativeness (whether actually by children or by those with childish minds), which, because it is less observed and therefore less influenced and controlled, is all the more authentic : wall scratchings, or *graffiti*. The art of the wall has been almost entirely neglected. Yet it is *graffiti* which, from the Neolithic caves to the cities of classical antiquity, have supplied the most exact and the most unsophisticated evidence on the character and intimate nature of a civilization.

They have been discovered abundantly on the house walls of Rome and Pompeii ; and even in our own day this genuine 'mural' art, with its odd world of signs, figures and symbols, continues to exist. In the year 1956 *graffiti* resembling those in the Dordogne caves, in the ancient Nile valley or in Mesopotamia, were still appearing on walls within a stone's throw of the Paris Opéra, in the heart of the city. I myself have for twenty years now been gathering the wild and frail blossoms of this art as they sprout up throughout the *faubourgs* of Paris.

The things about children's drawings that please us are their dreamlike fantasy, their naïvety, their humour, their closeness to the world of fairy tale, the happiness of their graphic inventions, their innate sense of colour. But there is a change of expression with the change of surface from paper to wall. By taking away the facility of pencil-on-paper the wall seems to obtain from the child-artist a quite different style—more astringent, harder, more expressive and, elaborations of detail being suppressed, less sweet.

As an area of blotches, cracks, coarse or decaying surfaces, crazing and damp patches, the texture of a wall is particularly apt to suggest images and to excite the imagination. Like the forms of rocks, of knots in wood and of mountains, which have always done so, wall surfaces are richly suggestive of shapes to the eye of man. Leonardo da Vinci had already perceived the *maieutic* properties of a wall, able unconsciously to conceive and deliver in the minds of beholders the forms which are inherent in it, when he wrote the celebrated passage in the *Treatise of Painting* :

> A variety of compositions may be seen in such spots, according to the disposition of the mind with which they are considered ; such as heads of men, various animals, battles, rocky scenes, seas, clouds, woods, and the like. It may be compared to the sound of bells, which may seem to say whatever we choose to imagine.

A child who at first had all his pleasure in scoring the wall with an old, blunt pen-knife and covering it with a chaos of meaningless lines will suddenly grow serious in his fun once he has recognized a *face* in a chance outline. This recognition is enough for a form to isolate itself from the scratchings and become the object of the child's vision. He needs only to give a *name* to the outline and he will feel he possesses, intoxicatingly, his own magic power as a creator of forms. One of my examples shows just one of these amorphous patches in which a child has recognized some sort of monster. By simply ringing it round he has lawfully taken possession of it—it has become his own creation. We are here looking at creation caught in the act.

We can also see how the growth and identification of the image of the human being in the child's mind is based on *cavities*, and not on *ovals*, as generally held by psychologists, who solidly maintain that the 'sausage-man' is the fundamental representation of a human. Again and again on the walls of Paris a *pair of holes* has been recognized by children as human eyes. Just two holes, but for the child it's a complete man, and his complete facial expression. More sinister than Melanesian masks, these dark pits watch us as it were from the depths of time. Later a third hole will be added to serve as a nose, and later still a fourth for the mouth. The final oval to enclose the manikin's moonlike face usually comes a good deal later, and is added by another hand. It is surprising that the same three or four holes can be given such a vast range of expression. It may, according to the child's own character that is being revealed, be anything between the extremes of jollity and tragedy. It is these solid and sombre works of art, cut down to essentials, in which the child has identified man at the same moment as for the first time expressing himself, which are perhaps the most moving of all, for they sweep us instantly into the uneasy world in which the soul of a child has its being.

The *graffiti* strike one by their extreme austerity, their primitive simplicity, the strictness of their composition. A child who on paper may fill up his scenes and stories with crowded detail is forced by the character of the wall to use a minimum of lines. He may also be helped by the freedom and impersonality of a wall to let himself go, to confess, to unburden himself of his troubles and anxieties, fears and obsessions. Like his far-distant ancestors the child struggles alone, in the darkness. Even now, the wall is a place preordained for ecstasies, for 'possession' by *Doppelgänger*. The emblems of love and death predominate. Numberless hearts, pierced by a line, marked with the loved one's initials—how often are they found pitted with holes, ravaged in a fit of fury or revenge ! Does this not recall the cave-man's painted bison, studded with arrows, by means of which the prehistoric hunter wanted to express his magical power, his 'siezing' ?

These same distresses and fears in early youth have given rise to a whole language of symbols. The widespread pierced-heart motif sometimes turns into a bow-and-arrows, or again the hammer-and-sickle, or a formalized version of the genital organs. Elsewhere the arrow may become a dagger, and the heart the thighs of a woman. Likewise, aeroplanes, torpedoes, pistols, streamlined motor cars may change into phallic emblems. We thus witness on the walls an unceasing transposition and transmutation of forms, disguising or altering themselves or sometimes reducing themselves to secret ideograms. We can follow almost step by step the birth of writing—for example, the ultimate simplification of the pierced-heart into a straight line intersecting a curved one. Or again, two lines making an X stand for death—are they the last vestiges of the skull and crossbones ? It was in this way that at the end of the Magdalenian period the pictures of a horse's head, a bison or a fish passed into geometrical outlines so abstract as to become unrecognizable as such.

The current language of the walls offers other analogies with the prehistoric past. It was surprising to discover in a squalid street the 'sister' of the well-known witch-doctor of the cave paintings, half man, half beast—the ancestor of later ages' fabulous monsters. There was a woman-headed bird, or better, a bird-headed woman, related to the beaked deities of the Assyrians and the ram, lion and hawk-headed gods of Egypt, who had been re-invented by some boy, probably because he had heard a woman called 'une poule' (a chicken, as prostitutes are popularly called in France). How ingeniously, too, had another artist, under the spell of the name 'Hilter' [sic], conjured a fully armed and helmed Teuton warrior, terrible to behold, goose-stepping a crude swastika into life.

It is also surprising to note to what degree the idea of death occupies the imagination of children. A vast variety of death's heads dominates the walls, but of course these also symbolize adventure, seafaring and piracy, and poison. There are a great many demons, sorcerers, fairies, ghosts and imaginary animals. To the war and the occupation are owed the warriors and the gallows.

The greater number of *graffiti* suggest the vanished civilizations of Central and South America, or still earlier epochs, such as the horned cattle found in the rue du Temple, which could easily have come from a cave in the Vallée d'Eyzie. Some *graffiti*, on the other hand, recall great artists of our own times ; Picasso is brought to mind by an amusing version of the death's head. A magician recalls Klee, and others Miró, while some of the tragic, mask-like faces have affinities with Rouault.

Translated by James Clark

The three major themes of the world of *graffiti* sum up all that matters in existence : birth, love, death. Birth —the entity 'man' picked out for the first time. Love —both carnal and sentimental. Death — both annihilation and great adventure. A latent animism is given expression in demons, witches, fairies, phallic deities and half-human monsters, among the more ordinary warriors, heroes and beasts. This mysterious, emblematic universe, complete with charms and spells, still persists under the neon-lit city sky.

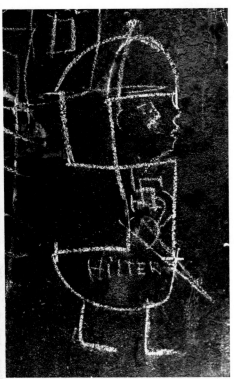

We are worlds away from the sweetness of child-art. All becomes earnest, raw, harsh, barbaric. It is usually an isolated being, a prey to anxious conflicts, whose hand scratches these lines. Childhood is no golden age, but the age of torment. A whole lifetime is sometimes not enough to wear away its scars. These tragic, and even hideous, masks bear witness to the suffering enclosed in the soul of a child.

The wall is an exorcism. Offering refuge to anything that is repressed, disapproved of, forbidden or oppressive, it is at the same time their catharsis. The child feels safe out of the watchful sight of adults; the anonymous wall will keep his secrets for him. This accounts for his preference for narrow alleyways, dark culs-de-sac, empty buildings, bomb-sites. All the examples reproduced with this article come from Paris, except for one from Istanbul.

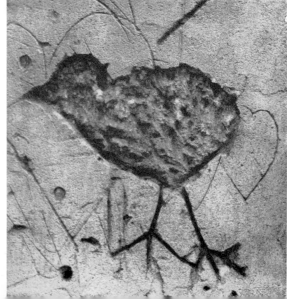

Their plastic quality is what at times lifts these *graffiti* to the kind of intensity and grandeur that belongs to the art of archaic civilizations. A plastic beauty that is quietly accentuated by physical and chemical agents. Damp, heat, and smoke coat and corrode the walls, ageing them so fast that they already seem to belong to antiquity.

THE PHILOSOPHY OF THE BED

by MARY EDEN

BEDS ARE a worthy subject for philosophers. We are born in bed, we die in bed, we spend a third of our lives in bed ; they are the scene of our sufferings in sickness and our pleasures in love ; yet philosophers have unaccountably neglected them. Perhaps, because most philosophers are men, they have feared that a theme so superficially frivolous might bring them into disrepute. As a woman I have been spared such inhibitions, and this must be my only excuse for making my present contribution to philosophic literature.

To the unromantic a bed is simply a piece of furniture, raised on four legs, and with a surface more or less adapted to the biological function of sleep. Those who think of beds in this way are to be pitied ; the subtleties of life escape them. Your true amateur of beds will see in them a symbol of all that is highest in man and which makes him

[251]

Opposite : L'Homme et la
Femme by Pierre Bonnard, 1900
Paris : Musée d'Art Moderne

Above : Le Lit, by Henri de
Toulouse-Lautrec. Paris: Louvre

Danaë, by Rembrandt, 1636. Leningrad : Hermitage

superior to the brutes. A bed is the emblem of our sophistication, and the proper use of it a criterion of civilized status.

Animals make beds, but it is doubtful if they realize their true significance. Even a bird's nest is a bed of a kind, and dogs instinctively revolve on an imaginary pile of straw before abandoning themselves to the pampered security of their baskets. There is something lacking in these processes, however ; they cannot be compared with the splendid abandonment to horizontality which can be enjoyed only by human beings.

The characteristic human bed has had a history as long as man, and was already evolving in the time of our Stone Age ancestors.

After many generations of scooping suitable repositories in the earth for their hips, some inventive genius among them must have grasped the sensual possibilities of a pile of skins; thereafter there was no looking back.

By the time of the first civilizations the importance of beds in the social pattern was firmly established. The Egyptian bed, for example, although possessing a wooden head-rest instead of a pillow, was surely the source of manifold delights, even before the time of Cleopatra. The Greeks and Romans were so enamoured of beds that they even extended their use to the daytime, and took all their meals in the horizontal position from a couch. It is doubtful, however, whether the average Greek bed was as comfortably pillowed and bolstered as that upon which Rembrandt painted the mythical Danaë, in her brazen tower, awaiting the arrival of Zeus. There is also a certain air of over-sophistication in Titian's bedroom appointments for 'The Venus of Madrid' (the organ-player, it is supposed, is a portrait of Prince Ottavio Farnese).

Some interesting facts concerning classical and medieval beds are recorded in Fosbroke's *Encyclopædia of Antiquities*. There we learn that the *grabatum* was a low, portable bed used by Roman slaves; the *scympodium* a cross between a bed and a chair; and the *gyrgatus* 'a bed used for lunatics when bound.' Beds are frequently mentioned in the Bible, and were by no means always regarded with the emotions of tight-lipped disapproval that they have inspired in latter-day Puritans.

Below : The Venus of Madrid, by Titian. Madrid : Prado

Solomon, as we know, was in every sense an expert on beds ; and even Job, who was nothing if not a pessimist, admitted that 'my bed shall comfort me, my couch shall ease my complaint.' There is also the mysterious threat in *Revelations* to throw Jezebel into a bed—rather like threatening a child with a visit to the Zoo, one would have thought.

Since these distant times empires and religions have come and gone, but the bed has retained its ancient prestige. A whole article could be written on the various physical adaptations it has undergone in different societies, but to pontificate on such matters would be tedious. The philosophical implications of the subject will be better served by discussing the various activities that go on in the bed.

The first of these is, of course, the act of being born—a solemn enough subject in all conscience, but one demanding a specialized interest in obstetrics. However, there is one aspect of childbirth that must be briefly mentioned. This is the odd practice, formerly widely observed, and still followed today by certain primitive peoples, of sending the *father* to bed when a child is to be born. It is known as the *couvade*.

One of the best descriptions of the *couvade* occurs in the Provençal poem *Aucassin and Nicolette*. The hero, Aucassin, comes to the palace of the King of Torelore, where he finds the king lying upon his bed.

Below : Sleep, by Gustave Corbet, 1866. Paris : Petit Palais

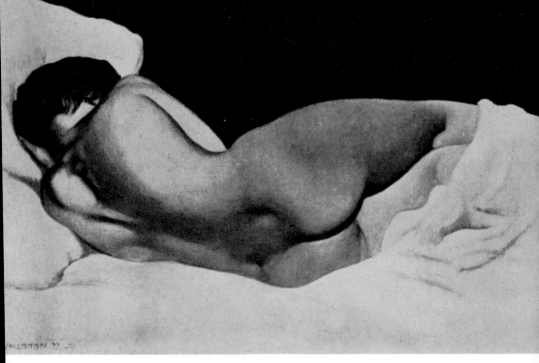

Reclining Nude, by Félix Vallotton, 1922. Paris : Rodrigues–Henriques Collection

When he asks what is the matter with him, he is told that he is expecting a son at the end of the month. In this, the king was only following a practice that has been reported by scientific investigators since the time of Strabo. Aucassin was no anthropologist, however, and instead of sympathizing with the agonies of paternity, he belaboured the king with a cudgel. Fortunately this does not seem to have brought on a miscarriage.

Once they have been born, and uttered their first cry at the misery of the world, the next act of most sensible infants is to go to sleep. The cradle, that claustrophobic second womb of the new-born child, may take many different forms, ranging from an elaborately ornamented basket, swathed in pink and blue ribbons, to a simple fish-net slung on the back of an Indian squaw.

Unlike children, for whom to be sent to bed is a punishment and who often have an unreasonable dread of nightmares, adults seem generally to be enthusiastic about sleep. In fact they are prone to carry the practice beyond the confines of the bed, and indulge in it in lecture

[255]

L'amant favorisé : engraving by Chaponnier after Boilly.
Victoria and Albert Museum

rooms, concert halls, and even churches. Some people, not content
with their normal nightly ration, have gone to sleep for protracted
periods. Thus in 1546 William Foxley, pot-maker to the Mint in the
Tower of London, went to sleep for fifteen days, and could not be
aroused even by pinching and burning. He eventually awoke duly
refreshed, and continued thereafter to sleep for normal periods.

Sleep may also be indulged in for purposes of publicity. In March,

1950, passers-by in Connecticut Avenue, Washington, were delighted to see an attractive young lady going to bed in a strapless nightdress in a shop window. She turned out to be the Beauty Queen of Washington, and her behaviour was not simply due to eccentricity ; it was designed to draw attention to a method of learning languages in one's sleep, sponsored by the Educational Services Organization.

Even more delightful than sleep, in the view of many, is the tender commerce of love. Although enjoyed by men and women since sophisticated pleasures first grew to be one of the fine blooms of our civilization, this is still regarded by some as an indelicate theme. Nevertheless the hurly-burly of the nuptial couch has inspired some of the finest works of art, music and literature in the world. Propertius, the greatest of the elegaic poets of Rome, even allows that the bed itself is hallowed by his joys :

'How happy is my lot ! O night that was not dark for me, and thou beloved couch, blest by my delight ! How many sweet words we interchanged, while the lamp was by, and how we strove together when the light was gone ! For now she struggled with me with breasts uncovered, now veiling herself in her tunic, checking my advance. With a kiss she unsealed mine eyes weighed down by slumber and said : "Dost thou lie thus, thou sluggard ?" How often we shifted our arms and varied our embrace ; how long my kisses lingered on her lips !'

Nor, contrary to certain old-fashioned beliefs, are such pleasurable emotions confined to the male sex. Throughout history many an unhappy damsel has lain forlornly in bed, aching for the caresses of an absent lover. We have only to think of Dido in the Idylls of Theocritus, unable to sleep for the raging love tormenting her breast, or the more tender, but no less passionate, heroine of the Song of Solomon who lamented : 'By night on my bed I sought him whom my soul loveth : I sought him, but I found him not.'

The more severe will insist that the pleasures of dalliance must be secondary to the true object of love, the procreation of children. Unfortunately, however, the blessed event does not always result, in which case men have at various times thought up expedients to ensure success. One of the most remarkable of these was the celebrated Celestial Magnetico-Electric Bed which in the late eighteenth century reposed in the Temple of Health at the Adelphi. This, which was described in detail in *The Saturday Book* a few years ago, was the property of a Dr. Graham, and, although on show to all who could afford to pay

five shillings a head at night and a mere half-crown in the day time, was nevertheless primarily recommended 'to their Excellencies the Foreign Ambassadors, to the Nobility, Gentry and to persons of Learning and Taste.' The sight of this rare object was accompanied by a lecture from Dr. Graham on the true effects of electricity, air, music and magnetism on the human body.

So popular did these lectures become (it is recorded on several evenings that there had been 'an overflow of at least nine hundred ladies and gentlemen') that the learned doctor was encouraged to higher flights. He made the bed available to any childless couple who wished to use it for £50 a session, announcing moreover that the bed-clothes were 'perfumed with the most costly essences of Arabia.'

That the use of such elaborate machinery was necessary at all can possibly be put down to the rather primitive attitude to courtship which has always prevailed in certain quarters. Too often wives have been chosen with a cavalier indifference to feminine sentiments. For instance in Aubrey's *Brief Lives*, we learn how Sir William Roper of Eltham came one day to select one of Sir Thomas More's daughters as a wife with the same kind of casual sensuality he might have bestowed on a carcase of beef. Aubrey writes :

'My lord's daughters were then both a-bed in a truckle-bed in their father's chamber asleep. He carries Sir into the chamber and takes the sheet by the corner and suddenly whippes it off. They lay on their backs, and their smocks up as high as their armpits. This awakened them, and immediately they turned on their bellies. Quoth Roper : "I have seen both sides," and so gave a pat on her buttock he made choice of, saying, "Thou art mine." Here was all the trouble of the wooeing.'

When one reads of More allowing this sort of thing one wonders what other goings on he would have tolerated in his Utopia.

Before leaving the subject of unromantic courtships, a word must be said about that oddest of all activities performed in bed—the art of bundling. According to the *Oxford English Dictionary* to bundle is 'to sleep on one's bed or couch *with* (as once was customary with persons of opposite sexes, in Wales and New England).' The first part of the definition is innocent enough, and most of us have been forced to bundle at some time or another, especially in war-time, when staying with relations, or in other dire emergencies. It is the sinister passage enclosed in brackets that must cause us to reflect.

Lest Welshmen and New Englanders should resent the suggestion of excessive purity I should state straight away that, in spite of the *Oxford English Dictionary*, bundling is not confined to their homelands alone. A correspondent of the *Daily Mail* found it being practised in the Orkneys as recently as 1941, 'a special, traditional, and very complicated knot' being tied round the ankles of the girl for bundling purposes. It is still also a popular pursuit in the island of Lewis in the Hebrides, where, instead of the ankle-knot, the girl's legs are inserted into a single large stocking which her mother ties above the knees.

The main purpose of bundling is to give young couples an opportunity of courting in climates where an insistence on 'walking out' might be sufficiently discouraging to depopulate the whole region. Bundling, it seems, in spite of the ankle-knots and stockings, has quite the opposite effect. Thus, according to Washington Irving, it helped the early settlers in America to produce in record time, 'a long-sided raw-boned hardy race of whoreson whalers, wood-cutters, fishermen and peddlers ; and strapping corn-fed wenches, who by their united efforts tended marvellously towards populating those notable tracts of country called Nantucket, Piscataway, and Cape Cod.' In spite of these recommendations, however, the practice receives the blessing neither of doctors nor ministers, and the youth of warmer climes must still be encouraged to content itself with the bed-less austerity of the circle at the Roxy.

We have now almost come to the last and most irrevocable natural act taking place in bed, that of dying in it. But before treating of this sombre matter we must briefly describe a few of the outstanding beds of the past, and touch on one further important social aspect of our theme. The most famous of all beds in England is certainly the Great Bed of Ware, which formerly stood at the Saracen's Head in that town, and is now in the Victoria and Albert Museum. Other historic beds, although smaller, have been at least equally interesting. For example, in the great exhibition of 1851, the catalogue contained an entry advertising the Savage Alarm Bedstead. The word Savage, incidentally, did not refer to the quality of the alarm, but was the name of the bed's designer, a certain Mr Robert Watson Savage. The workings of the bed do not seem to have been recorded, but it was probably similar to another equally unattractive contraption that was exhibited some years later at the Leipzig Fair. This incorporated two pre-set alarms, after which a board appeared before the occupant's eyes reading 'Time to Get Up.' If this stern injunction was disregarded the bed then snatched its victim's night cap from his head and removed the bed clothes. By this time, however, even the bed was beginning to show signs of compassion, for its last act was to light a

Above, the Great Bed of Ware, c. 1580. Victoria and Albert Museum

Below : Hand-made bedroom furniture designed for Heal's by Nigel Walters

Tobias and Sara. German stained glass, c. 1530. Victoria and Albert Museum

candle and a spirit stove to assist in the making of an early morning cup of tea.

More recently an even more elaborate robot bed was constructed to assist Mr Howard Hughes, the millionaire film producer, get over the effects of a plane crash. Hughes was totally incapacitated, but his bed, which was powered by thirty electric motors, made up for his every deficiency. The controls were mounted on an elaborate dashboard, and, among other things, the bed would produce hot and cold water at will, and convey its occupant about the room at a touch of the appropriate button.

There are numerous records of beds of odd shape. Ludwig II of Bavaria paid £100,000 to have one made in the form of a cathedral, and according to Reginald Reynolds, that prince of bed philosophers, a famous American film actress who has been married four times has a bed in the shape of a heart. A former mayor of Birmingham (Alabama, not Warwickshire) commanded that a circular bed should be made for him for the sound reason that he lived in a circular house (whether he himself was circular is not stated) ; this led to his undoing, however, for the exoticism of the setting prompted him constantly to eat peanuts before going to sleep, whereupon his wife very properly divorced him.

Indian Miniature : A Prince dallying with Ladies on a Bed, c. *1720*
Victoria and Albert Museum

[263]

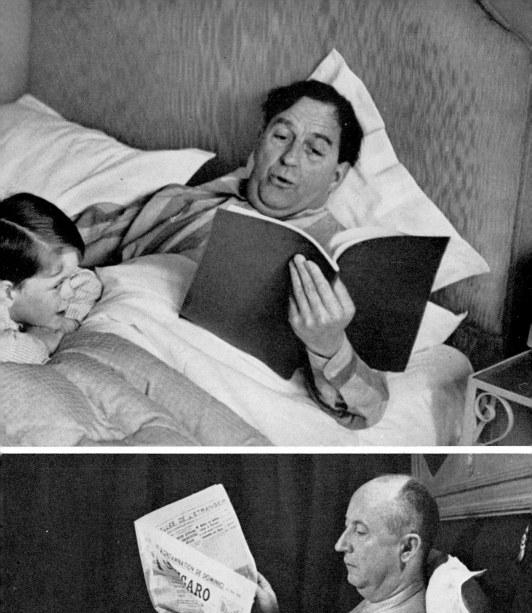
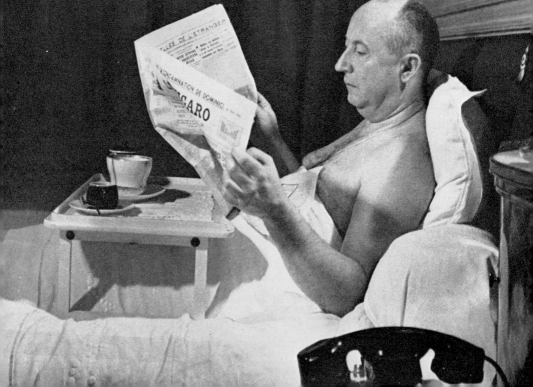

I must turn now to my final piece of bed sociology—the *lit de parade*. This expression originated in the ancient custom of a woman holding court in bed after the birth of a child, but later acquired a wider significance and developed a special ritual. The visitors were expected to bring lavish presents, and the hospitality extended to them became increasingly extravagant. The occasion also provided an opportunity for the lying-in mother to array herself in the richest and most seductive garments and to deck her bedroom with expensive silk and satin

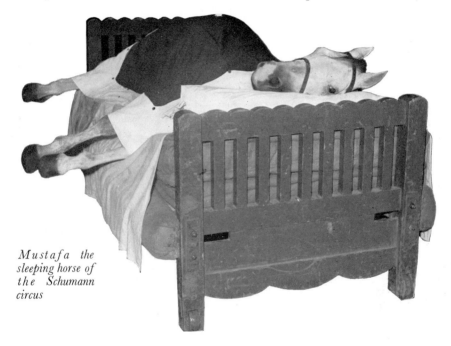

Mustafa the sleeping horse of the Schumann circus

hangings. Thus a letter written in the early seventeenth century tells how the Countess of Salisbury 'was brought a bed of a daughter and lyes in very richly, for the hangings of her chamber . . . is valued at fourteen thousand pounds.'

Unchivalrously, the husbands who had to provide such innocent indulgences eventually began to count the cost. In fact in some countries legislation was passed prohibiting any excessive ostentation on the *lit de parade*. In Milan, for example, women were not allowed to use counterpanes of embroidered silk, or stitched with gold or silver thread, nor to wear silk camisoles when receiving callers.

In later times the use of the *lit de parade* was not limited to the period

[265]

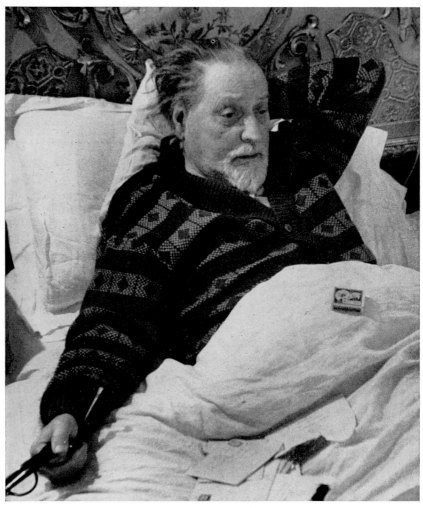

Sir Compton Mackenzie receiving visitors

immediately after childbirth. Madame de Montespan retired to bed
to receive compliments on the marriage of her niece, while one well-
known actress of my acquaintance still adopts this procedure on the
morning following her first nights. The *lit de parade* can also be a symbol
of determined femininity in distress. Only a few years ago, on receiving
an urgent call from a titled lady enjoying her third bankruptcy, I
found her serenely installed on her *lit de parade* (the only article of
furniture left) dispensing gin to the bailiffs out of potted paste pots.

A variant of the *lit de parade* is employed also by men, but being of the more pompous sex they prefer to call it the *lit de justice*. This phrase originated, it is believed, in France (a land which really understands beds) in the fourteenth century, when the king used to attend his parliament lying on a couch. It has been employed extensively since, particularly by writers such as Sir Compton Mackenzie and Sir Winston Churchill, and television personalities such as Mr Gilbert Harding, who often receives visitors in the recumbent or semi-recumbent position. It is strange how the judgements made from this point of vantage always seem to gain in authority and weight.

It is not supposed to be glorious to die in bed, but I can see no reason for this prejudice. Instead of falling messily on some foreign field for an abstraction called national honour, it is surely better to go forth, serenely horizontal, on the couch that has been the scene of so many poignant emotions—childhood fears and longings, youthful strength in love, the deeper and more tempestuous passions of maturity? We cannot, unfortunately, choose when we are going to die, but most of us are able to choose where, and I can see no reason to die anywhere but in bed. Why not enjoy one's death where one has enjoyed so much of one's life? Perhaps also one's deathbed is the only place where the profounder philosophy of the bed will be properly understood.

The conception of Alexander : Nectanebus (right) as a dragon reassumes his human shape for the seduction of Olimpias. From a fifteenth century MS in the British Museum

Jeffrey Hudson. Engraving after the painting by Daniel Mytens

THE NATURAL HISTORY OF

THE DWARF

by RICHARD CARRINGTON

THE CULT of dwarfs, like the cult of giants, owed its origin to man's capacity for wonder ; but the appeal of the small to the human imagination is very different from the appeal of the large. Whereas giants axiomatically inspire fear and awe, dwarfs must be content to arouse a half-affectionate, half-contemptuous curiosity. A student of dwarf natural history must not ignore these facts, for they explain much of the characteristic behaviour of dwarfs—their overflowing energy and their pugnacity, for example. It is difficult to face life with serenity if one inhabits a private Lilliputian world below waist level and is in constant danger of being trodden on.

It is as well to be clear at the outset exactly what is meant by a dwarf, for there is some confusion on the question. Normal people of exceptionally small stature are sometimes called dwarfs, usually with the intention of insulting them. Thus Lysander in *A Midsummer Night's Dream* says to Hermia : 'Get you gone, you dwarf !' This is, of course, a misuse of the word, although it underlines the kind of discourtesies that real dwarfs have to put up with. Again, some people confuse small races of men, such as the pygmies, with dwarfs, although their diminutive stature is a natural outcome of the evolutionary process.

A true dwarf owes his small size to one of several pathological causes. Medical science can say very little about these even today, but dwarfs can usually be placed in one of three categories. First, there is the true homunculus or midget—the perfectly formed little man or woman who may nevertheless be only two or three feet high. The cause of the condition in this case is usually a relatively inactive pituitary gland. The second type of dwarfism is due to differences in the growth rate of the membrane and cartilage bones, causing retarded development of the limbs. Thirdly, there are several kinds of seriously deformed dwarfs, who may even lack limbs altogether ; but these last are mainly of medical interest and will not be discussed at length here.

Our prehistoric ancestors, we may be sure, were merciless to dwarfs, despising them for their unusual appearance, and killing them ruthlessly as weaklings who would be a burden to the tribe. As society became more sophisticated, and a wealthy and leisured aristocracy arose, the ruling class came to regard dwarfs as an amusing curiosity. They were much sought after as court buffoons, and troops of dwarfs were brought in after state banquets for the diversion of the king and his guests. The custom was introduced from Egypt and the East, and by Roman times dwarfs had reached such a peak of popularity that they were being imported into Europe from all parts of the known world. According to Suetonius, Augustus Caesar used to play with his dwarfs for nuts, and thus learned to forget his natural melancholy and the cares of state. Domitian even kept a band of dwarf gladiators, who were matched against suitably handicapped men of normal size as a spectacle in the arena.

The fascination of real dwarfs was augmented by many picturesque superstitions. 'Little men' played an important part in European mythology of all ages, and still do in the mythologies of primitive tribes. They were supposed to originate in an independent dwarf kingdom, which obeyed its own laws and was ruled over by a dwarf king. The members of this kingdom, it was said, were either goose-footed or duck-footed, and some even had their feet on backwards, so their gait was uncertain. They always preferred to wear grey or green clothing, and sported red caps with long, tapering points. The caps could make them invisible at will, and the true dwarf virtuosos, for some unspecified reason, had a weakness for turning themselves into toads.

Travellers, who have an enthusiasm for tall stories shared only by fishermen, often brought back the strangest tales of dwarfs from foreign parts. For example, Sir John Mandeville, who travelled in Asia and Africa between 1322 and 1356, told of a race of little men who had no mouths, but only a small, round hole through which they sucked their nourishment with a pipe. There was also a sixteenth-century report by the Italian traveller Antonio Pigaffetta, obviously of equal authenticity, of dwarfs in the Moluccas whose ears were so large that they slept on one and covered their bodies with the other.

The character of the mythological dwarf was mischievous, but on the whole benevolent. He was industrious, and spent long hours at his forge in the mountains, for he was reputed to be a splendid smith. He was also fond of cooking, and could be persuaded to help larger human housewives with their kitchen chores if suitably bribed. But if there was mist anywhere near the dwarf holes in the mountains, he could on no account be disturbed, for he was then busy forging and cooking on his own behalf, and would obviously resent interruption. It was always inadvisable to irritate a dwarf or he might start thieving, or even kidnapping one's children.

England, of course, possesses her own famous mythological dwarf in Tom Thumb, who appears in the Arthurian legends ; but he is of less interest than a real member of the tribe, named Jeffrey Hudson, who was page to Charles I and whose adventurous life would have been sufficiently exciting for a man at least four times his size. Hudson, who was born at Oakham in Rutland in 1619, was one of the earliest English dwarfs of whom we have an authentic record. His fame was such that a plaque was put up to him in Newgate Street and he was later introduced by Sir Walter Scott into his novel *Peveril of the Peak*. Hudson's parents were of normal size, the father being 'a very proper man, broad-shouldered and chested,' and the mother likewise 'of no mean altitude.' But at the age of nine he was only eighteen inches tall, although excellently proportioned and without any trace of deformity. According to his own assertions he did not add another inch to his stature until he was thirty, when he suddenly grew to a height of three feet nine inches. Unfortunately, there are sound medical reasons why this part of the story cannot be entirely true ; changes in the bones of the skeleton make any considerable growth impossible after the age of twenty. But it is certainly likely that Hudson retained his exceptionally small stature until he was well into his teens.

While still a boy, Hudson entered the service of the Duchess of Buckingham, where he was greatly pampered, being dressed in silks and satins, and introduced to all the duchess's noble friends. Shortly after the marriage of Charles I and Henrietta Maria, the royal couple were entertained to a banquet by the duchess, who decided to surprise her guests by a novel diversion. Hudson was placed inside a cold pie, which was put on the table in front of the king and queen. As it was about to be cut, he popped up through the crust dressed as a soldier and flourished his sword. The queen was so delighted by this drollery that the duchess presented the dwarf to her, and he was made a member of the royal court. Here, it is recorded, he struck up a friendship with William Evans, the king's gigantic porter. One of Evans's favourite acts at the court entertainments was to produce a slice of cheese from one pocket and, with feigned astonishment, Hudson instead of a loaf of bread from the other.

The king eventually knighted his dwarf, and began to employ him on confidential missions, for Hudson was a man of great intelligence. In 1630 he was sent to France to fetch a midwife for Henrietta Maria, and on the return journey was involved in an exciting adventure. Pirates attacked the ship near Dunkirk, Hudson being taken prisoner and sold into slavery. He was next heard of in Turkey, but was redeemed by the king and returned to England. He always attributed his sudden increase in height to the hardships he experienced at this time.

When the civil wars began, Hudson became a captain of horse in the royal army, and in 1644 accompanied the queen to France. Here he became involved in a dispute with a Mr Crofts, the brother of Lord Crofts, and challenged him to a duel. Crofts accepted, but took the matter so lightly that he arrived at the duelling ground armed only with a squirt. Deeply angered by this insult, Hudson shot his adversary dead on the spot, an offence for which he was imprisoned and expelled from the court. Even then his adventurous career was not over, for he was later confined to the Gate-house in Westminster for suspected conspiracy in the Popish plot. He died in 1682, shortly after his release, aged sixty-three.

Hudson was probably a pituitary dwarf, for his body showed no signs of deformity. In this, he was in marked contrast to another seventeenth-century dwarf who acquired almost equal fame. This was Matthew Buchinger of Ansbach, who must strictly be regarded not as a dwarf, but as a medical freak. He had no hands, feet, legs or thighs, and his arms were mere stumps, resembling the fins of a fish more than the arms of a man. He was thus little more than a trunk, measuring just under thirty inches in height.

For a person born with such grave disadvantages Buchinger's achievements were astonishing. He excelled in calligraphy, of all unexpected things, and in a contemporary exhibition bill it was claimed for him that :

> He makes a pen and writes several hands as quick and well as any writing master, and will write with any for a wager. . . . He threads a fine needle very quick ; shuffles a pack of cards, and deals them very swift. He plays upon the dulcimer as well as any musician ; he does many surprizing things with cups and balls, and gives the curious great satisfaction thereby ; he plays at skittles several ways very well ; shaves himself very dextrously ; and many other things too tedious to insert.

Not the least of Buchinger's achievements was to be married four times, and to produce eleven children, all of normal size. His writing was so exquisite and precise that he once succeeded in drawing a picture of himself with the full text of the 27th, 121st, 128th, 140th, 149th, and 150th Psalms, as well as the Lord's Prayer, inscribed among the curls of his wig. How so deformed a person was able to produce work of this quality is unknown, but its authenticity is proved by the existence of the Buchinger texts among the Harleian manuscripts at the British Museum.

The third type of dwarf, whose small stature is dependent on differences in relative bone growth, is well represented by the Dutchman Wybrand Lolkes, who was born at Jelst in West Friesland in 1730. He had a large head and exceptionally short arms and legs and, when full grown, stood only twenty-seven inches high. He first took up the profession of watchmaker, but soon found he could live more profitably by exhibiting himself. At his public appearances he was always accompanied by his exceptionally tall wife, and it was noticeable that even when Lolkes reached upwards to the greatest extent to take her hand she had difficulty in reaching it without stooping. In spite of this discrepancy in size the marriage seems to have been a success, for it was blessed with three children, one of whom grew to nearly six feet.

Male dwarfs appear to be more common than females (although this may simply be because more accounts of them have been preserved), but dwarfism in women has been recorded on several occasions. For example, in the Hunterian Museum at the Royal College of Surgeons there is the skeleton of the delightful little dwarf known as Caroline Crachami, who stood only 22½ inches high and who must have weighed in life well under half a stone. She died in 1824, at the age of nine years, the pathological causes of her dwarfism being regarded as quite different from those applying to all other dwarfs. In fact, she was responsible for giving medicine the name of a new disease —*ateleiosis*, or 'not arriving at perfection.' An even more remarkable female dwarf, born in Corsica in 1743, was Madame Teresia, the Corsican Fairy. She was admirably proportioned, being some thirty-four inches high and weighing about twenty-six pounds. This dwarf was twice exhibited in London, and delighted her visitors with her elegant, fairy-like appearance and her spirited conversation, which she conducted in Italian and French.

The most famous of all dwarfs is probably the Pole, Joseph Boruwlaski, later known as Count Boruwlaski, who was born near Chahez in Polish Russia in 1739. He came from humble parents, but his small stature (at the age of fifteen he was only twenty-five inches high) soon attracted the attention of the neighbouring landowners, and he was taken successively into the homes of the Starosta de Caorlix and the Countess Humiecka. The latter became his patron, and in the aristocratic environment of her home he learnt to acquire something of the culture and *savoir faire* which, in those days, were associated with people of noble birth. Later, with the adopted title of count, he toured Europe with his benefactress, making a great stir wherever he went.

After visiting Vienna and receiving the favours of the Empress Maria Theresa, he arrived in triumph at Paris. Here he was received as an equal at the French court, and the nobility vied with each other to give banquets in his honour. At one of these the plates, dishes, glasses and cutlery were proportioned to Boruwlaski's size, and even the food consisted of small things, such as ortolans and beccaficos. While the dwarf was in Paris an interesting account of him was sent by Count Tressan to the French Academy of Sciences ; Boruwlaski was at this time twenty-two years of age and about twenty-eight inches high. Tressan writes :

> He is well proportioned, and has nothing shocking about him ; his eyes are fine and full of fire ; his features agreeable, and his physiognomy spirited, which indicates the gaiety and sprightliness of his mind. He enjoys a perfect state of health, drinks nothing but water, eats little, sleeps well, and can bear a great deal of fatigue. He dances well, and is very nimble ; his judgement is sound, and his heart susceptible of the most tender impressions. He loves to be treated with the decorum due to his rank, yet is not offended with those who make free with him on account of his stature.

Boruwlaski's 'susceptible heart' led him on occasion into difficulties. After an unsuccessful attempt to win the hand of a French actress he was very nearly abandoned by his benefactress, who was very jealous of his attentions to other women. He was, in fact, dismissed her service as the result of another such affair, this time with a young girl named Isalina Barbutan, who was also in the countess's employ. This romance had a happy ending, however, for the dwarf eventually married Isalina. He spent his later years touring Europe giving concerts, for he was a fine performer on the guitar, and died eventually at Durham, at the advanced age of 98 years.

Although few dwarfs have shown the fine feeling and artistic sensibility of Boruwlaski, several have been men of high ability. Whereas gigantism is usually accompanied by feebleness of mind, there is no reason why a dwarf should not be as mentally capable as a man of normal stature. For example, the famous Italian dwarf Bertholde actually became Prime Minister to the King of Lombardy, and was the king's constant adviser on personal matters as well as affairs of state. Other dwarfs have shown remarkable astuteness in business, or proved their courage in military affairs. Thus Richebourg, the last dwarf to hold office at the French court, was employed to take dispatches abroad during the Revolution. He was disguised as a child, and could travel in places where a full-grown man would have aroused suspicion.

The high intelligence often associated with dwarfs does not, of course, mean that they are not sometimes as eccentric as other members of the human race. One of the most appealing examples of dwarf eccentricity was reported in the *Daily Telegraph* for September 17, 1867. It concerned a little French dwarf, 'immensely old, and wonderfully diminutive,' who was supposed to have spent more than half his life riding on omnibuses. He would leave his home each morning at seven and immediately board an omnibus. On reaching the terminus he would change to another route, and thus ride about Paris all day with short breaks for lunch and dinner. He did not go home until late at night, always contriving to obtain a ticket for the last omnibus, which went at midnight, from the Palais Royal to the Barrière du Trône. On every journey he would obtain, if possible, a seat just inside the door so he could chat with the conductor. One of his eccentricities was that he would always take a *correspondance* ticket, entitling him to travel all day on different omnibuses for the same price ; but this he never made use of, preferring to pay afresh at the beginning of each ride. He lived alone, and was obviously possessed of a considerable fortune. When at last he died, and an inventory was taken of his effects, one of his drawers was found to contain fifteen hundred omnibus *correspondance* tickets, all carefully sorted and labelled. The theory put forward to explain the strange mania of this dwarf was that he imagined himself to be a secret inspector of omnibuses, whose duty it was to report the number of passengers in each vehicle, so as to detect possible frauds by omnibus conductors.

No account of the natural history of the dwarf would be complete without some mention of the self-styled 'General' Tom Thumb, the American dwarf who took London by storm in the fourth decade of the nineteenth century. His real name was Charles S. Stratton, and he was born at Bridgeport, Connecticut, on January 11, 1832. The history of his growth was unusual. At birth he weighed nine pounds two ounces, which is much above the average for a normal human infant. At five months he weighed about fifteen pounds, and measured twenty-five inches in height. But then he stopped growing entirely for over twelve years, and at fourteen was only a few ounces heavier than he had been at five months.

Tom Thumb was first exhibited in Barnum's old American Museum in New York, where he made a tremendous success. Then, after a triumphal tour of the United States, he sailed in January, 1844, for England, where he was received in audience by Queen Victoria. While in London he had built for himself a miniature coach measuring only twenty inches high and eleven inches wide. This was drawn by a pair of tiny Shetland ponies, and two boys were engaged as coachman and footman. The following year the General took his equipage across the Channel, and scored further royal successes with Louis Philippe of France, and Queen Isabella of Spain.

The General's income went up in proportion to his fame, and his receipts in Europe amounted to over £100,000. His new-found wealth enabled him to indulge expensive tastes, and he developed a passion for chain-smoking large cigars ; he also spent much of his fortune on yachts and horses. All this time he was still working for Barnum, and the showman's joy must have been complete when Tom Thumb fell in love with another dwarf, named Lavinia Warren, who accepted his proposal of marriage. The wedding, which took place in 1863, was the signal for a publicity spree seldom seen even in the United States. The streets around the church were blocked for hours, and journalists, in their anxiety to do justice to the occasion, almost forgot the Civil War.

Tom Thumb died in 1883, at the age of 51. He was the last of the great dwarfs, for as society has evolved it has begun to sicken of wonders that are based on human abnormalities. That these exist is recognized, but they are regarded nowadays as a cause for compassion rather than idle curiosity. Whether General Tom Thumb, with his ample income and luxurious life, or Count Boruwlaski, with his glittering career among the crowned heads of Europe, would have agreed with this opinion is not known ; but to most people of sensibility, the decline of the dwarf cult will, I think, be a welcome sign that man is growing more civilized, more kindly, and more humane.

THE ROYAL ACATEMY

Mother and Daughter

PICTURES OF THE YEAR

No. 456

Father and Son

No. 789   Trompe l'œil

No. 987   *The Duchess*

No. 654   *Aunt Tabitha*

No. 321   'Archie'

No. 234

Evensong

No. 567   'So long as they're happy'

The Editor of THE SATURDAY BOOK *expresses*
his thanks to MR ARCHIE MASON *for his skilled*
assistance in the reproduction of these paintings.

A TRIFLE FROM S.E.17

by FRED BASON

As a great treat to myself on my birthday, August 29, 1927, I bought a seat in the circle (instead of the gallery) and witnessed one of the finest acting performances I have seen in many years of playgoing. I saw Robert Loraine in *The Father* by Strindberg. After the show I went round to the stage door to obtain the autograph of Mr Loraine.

Mr Loraine had been a brave soldier in the First World War, besides being a pioneer aviator. He was also a kindly man, and he made no bones about giving me his autograph. As he was signing my album he said to me, 'I don't go very much for this autograph hobby but I've often wanted to possess the autograph of Strindberg ; it would be nice to put it amongst my souvenirs.' Immediately I said to him : 'Well ! That's *easy* ; you just tell me where the bloke lives and I will get it for you. No one has ever yet refused my request, and when I tell Strindberg how much I've enjoyed *The Father* I am sure he'll oblige. I'll get it twice—once for you and once for me.'

Robert Loraine stared at me a moment, and then said he thought the dramatist lived in Barton Street, Westminster, when he was in Town. He thought the number was 7. So I thanked him politely, and said he'd have it in a day or so.

The next evening I made myself particularly tidy and walked from 152 Westmoreland Road, Walworth, S.E.17 (where I still live today) to 7 Barton Street, Westminster, S.W.1, to find Mr Strindberg. Number seven, unlike No. 152, had a distinguished Georgian façade. I

knocked, and a maid came to the door. I explained my quest. She was sure Mr Strindberg did not reside there, but she said she would ask the mistress and would I wait a few moments. Eventually a handsome lady came and said she was so sorry I'd had a journey for nothing ; Mr Strindberg has *moved*. Yes, she happened to know the address. It was in a block of flats off Tottenham Court Road. She put down the address on a slip of paper.

I'd got half-way up Charing Cross Road when I met a friend of mine named Mr Lupane, who at one time had been estate manager to Beatrice Lillie. I told him where I was going and he said he'd be delighted to accompany me, just for the walk. I was glad of his company for he was a nice old man. We were just at the top of Charing Cross Road when I met another pal of mine, Harry Saunders, who I knew to be a keen autograph collector, so I told him we were going to see Strindberg and maybe he'd like to come along with us.

Eventually we got to the block of flats. I was rather dismayed to find the number we sought was on the fourth floor and there was no lift ! Up and up we trooped. Poor Mr Lupane had to stop twice, for he was winded. When we got to the fourth floor we sat on the stone steps to get our breath back. We planned a manner of approach. I would do the talking, and when the dramatist was signing the card for Robert Loraine, Harry would put forward his own album and say, 'Please would you mind signing my album as well ?' Then Stanley Lupane would put forward my album and ask, 'Would you mind signing this one— please ?'

I knocked at the door. No answer. I knocked twice. To the door came an elderly man with snow-white hair. He looked just the sort of man to write *The Father*. He looked artistic, foreign and a dramatist (just as Paderewski always looked a pianist). I took off my cap and bowed (yes, I bowed). Then I said : 'Would you graciously honour us with your autograph, Mr Strindberg ? It will be truly appreciated.'

He said that he was not Mr Strindberg, he was not famous at all. I thought this to be false modesty. I said : 'Oh ! sir, you *are* famous, and all we want you to do is to write "August Strindberg" and the date in our albums. This post card is for Robert Loraine. After all, sir, he is the star of *your* play.'

He wavered for a moment, and then said that if it would really give us any pleasure, he would write 'August Strindberg' and the date, as we seemed bent on it. But he made the point that he would not sign in ink—only in pencil ! First he autographed the card, then Harry's book, and finally the book that Stanley Lupane put forward on my behalf.

There is a great personal satisfaction in capturing a difficult autograph. In forty years I've collected 11,193 different signatures of the famous and infamous—and only had 14 refusals in all this time.

The signing done, Mr Lupane made his way downstairs, followed by Harry. I lingered in order to shake the master's hand, and to congratulate him, very sincerely, on *The Father*. Then I bowed, all polite-like, and turned to follow my friends downstairs. I was half-way down

the first flight when I looked back and there was Mr Strindberg staring down, so I waved him a cheerful 'Good-bye.' I really was a happy collector at that moment.

Mr Strindberg suddenly called : 'Come back ! Come back *at once*— call to your friends. All of you— come back—*please* !' I called down-stairs to my pals, and eventually we were all together again on the land-ing outside Number 16. We hadn't the slightest idea what was going to happen. The nice old man asked us back into his flat. I hoped that he was going to show us the manuscript of *The Father* and give us each a glass of lemonade.

Mr Strindberg went over to the bookcase and took down from it a large octavo book bound in bright blue cloth, which he put upon the table. He then started to thumb through its pages. We stood waiting.

'Ah ! Here it is,' he said. 'Please listen very *carefully* whilst I read to you. "Johan August Strindberg was born in the year 1849. He was the most outstanding and prolific writer in Swedish literature. He died"— *note that, gentlemen*—"he died in 1912 following a brain operation"—note that, gentlemen—"*brain* operation !" You are fifteen years too late.'

We looked at each other. The penny dropped. I wished the floor could swallow me up. I had been kidded all along the line. I felt proper daft.

Out loud I said slowly : 'He died following a brain operation. Blimey ! I reckon I best go and have me own head examined right away. To have been taken in like this !'

I turned to Mr Lupane and said : 'Didn't *you* know the old cock was dead ?' No, he hadn't the slightest idea. Quite out of his line of country. 'Besides,' he said, 'when you tell me you are going to meet Mr Strindberg, naturally I assume the man hasn't been dead fifteen years !' He had a point there.

Then Harry got annoyed and said to the old man : 'So you've messed up a page in my album with a forged signature !' The old man got a piece of indiarubber from a brass ink-stand and said : 'That can easily be remedied. Rub it out ! That's why I insisted on using a pencil.'

Harry rubbed it out. 'It has been a good joke,' said the old man, 'but it's gone far enough. You, my boy [he said to me] were so polite that I simply could not allow you to become a laughing-stock. Let's all have a sherry and forget the whole thing !'

But I had to ask him how he came into the picture. He pointed to the telephone and said his friend in Barton Street had rung him up and explained that a young chap would come round asking for an autograph of Strindberg, and he was to pass him on to another of his friends not *too* far away—say Hampstead—and then ring his Hampstead friend and tell him of the plot and pass him on to someone somewhere else. Mr Robert Loraine was fond of practical jokes.

We drank our glass of sherry and parted the best of friends. I never saw Harry again, but Mr Lupane remained friendly for another twenty years.

I got on a bus, rode down to the Strand, and walked to the Savoy Theatre. I had to wait about forty minutes for the play to end. I told the stage door manager I had a gift for Mr Loraine. Eventually I was again in his dressing-room. 'There you are, Strindberg's autograph, all genuine, and dated 1927. I've been to HEAVEN to get the bleeding thing for you ! And I walked blooming miles. All the way from Walworth to Westminster and then right up to Tottenham Court Road,

and then up four blooming flights of stairs ! I'm tired out !'

He got up from his dressing-table. He must have been well over six feet, and thirteen stone of solid frame. I was just over five feet four, and not a pound over seven stone. I felt like giving him a bomp on his stately nose.

He said: 'So you're tired out. Exactly ! You've had some exercise. Exactly ! You looked to me last night in need of exercise. I have given you a little exercise ! You were also so cocksure that Mr Strindberg would oblige *you*.'

At that I pointed out that I had jumped at the opportunity to oblige *him*. Whereupon he asked me to shake hands with him and forget the whole thing. I shook hands—and then asked him for an autographed photograph by way of compensation. From a drawer in his dressing-table he got out a photo and signed it. (I still have it thirty-one years later.) He then got his dresser to take my book (and myself to go with him to see they were all alive) and we captured the signatures of Dorothy Dix, Lawrence Hanray, Milton Rosmer and Haidee Wright. A very satisfactory half-hour !

The next evening I went back to Barton Street to see the handsome lady who had sent me on the wild goose chase, stage two.

The maid opened the door. 'Oh ! Good evening. I have a nice gift for your mistress who was so kind to me.' Would I go in and wait? She'd see if Madam would be able to see me. As I waited I wrote in ink above the forged Strindberg autograph : 'With compliments to a handsome lady. Your slave for ever !'

When Madam arrived I did a little bow and handed over the autograph without a word. She looked at it, and then at me, and seemed quite lost for words. 'As you'd been so very kind last night to misdirect me to August Strindberg I felt I had to bring back a souvenir of the meeting with him.' Then — I laughed. And she laughed—she had a lovely laugh. We both laughed. The tears came into our eyes.

She asked if I would care to stay to dinner. She had two friends with her but I was not to mind them. She'd be most happy if I would stay. She felt I deserved something for taking it all in such a nice way. I pointed out that my clothes were shabby and I wasn't really fit to dine with posh people. 'Oh! That's nonsense,' she said, 'you just come in and make yourself at home.'

So I put my cap on a hallstand and followed her into a magnificent room, where there were two men, both around 50 years old, with steel grey hair, and well groomed. One was a Colonel and the other was a Doctor, but I didn't grasp the names.

The two men got into some sort of conversation and I stood looking at a big oil painting as Madam went out of the room. Then one of the men asked what I did for my living. I told them that I was what is called in my trade a 'book-runner.' They wanted to know what a book-runner was and I had to explain that I bought books in one part of London, repaired them, and then *ran* with them to where they were wanted.

One of the men then asked what sort of books I mainly sold. I was just going to answer him when Madam came back with a long bottle and some glasses. 'Oh!' she said, 'so you are a bookseller by day and an autograph collector by night?' 'Yes, madam—and no regrets.' 'Well! What *do* you sell?' I told them that I mostly sold novels that were out of print to public libraries. One of the men then asked me who were my most wanted authors, or most wanted novels. I told them that my three best sellers, the books I could at that time sell easier than any others, were *King Solomon's Mines* by Rider Haggard, *Of Human Bondage* by Somerset Maugham, and *The Blue Lagoon* by H. de Vere Stacpoole.

They looked at each other as if I had said something astounding. But I had merely made a statement of fact.

The lady looked at one of the men —and so did the other man. Since they both looked at him, I looked as well—but he was an entire stranger to me. One thing I did know : he wasn't Strindberg.

Then the lady said : 'Didn't you hear this gentleman's name when I introduced you?' 'No, mam, I can't say I did. It sounded foreign-like.' 'But, my dear boy, this gentleman *is* H. de Vere Stacpoole.'

'Are you really and honestly the author of *The Blue Lagoon*?' I asked.

The man took from his pocket a used envelope, and there was the name on the envelope. Out came my autograph album, and Mr Stacpoole signed his name in it. He told me that I had paid him the nicest compliment of his writing life, and if I'd give him my address he would send me one of his novels autographed especially for me.

He sent *The City Under the Sea*, with a long inscription in it. The blitz destroyed it at my home in 1941. Mr Stacpoole has been dead for some years now. In the past thirty years I have never come upon another autograph collector with this author's signature.

And in the past thirty years I've only once had as good a dinner as I had that night.

Cinderella

or

GLASS

SKATE

PLAICE

READY AT

by

BY ROAD. RAIL or SEA.

TAKING ALL RISK.

OLIVE COOK &
EDWIN SMITH

RAILWAY AGENTS & CARMEN.
NEWPORT IW & SOUTHAMPTON.

Place Your Hand in Mine, Wife.

A gentleman took for his second wife the most haughty woman

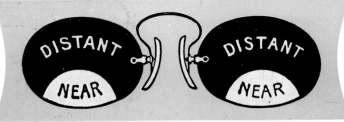

that ever was seen.

She had two daughters just like herself.

had to do the meanest tasks of the house.

The man's own daughter

Housework Easy Without Nagging Backache

She sat among the cinders

while her sisters made themselves fine.

decided to throw a ball.

The prince

The sisters were invited.

Cinderella had to help them dress.

They spent hours getting ready.

CENTURY BATH

Can you give me a really good plan for getting ready for a party? To me it either means a last-minute rush or too much time to work up 'party jitters'.

I FIND THIS A PERFECT FORMULA: Time allowed—one hour. After an all-over wash or a bath have a cold sponge down and finish with a cologne friction and then deodorant. Use cologne to set oily hair quickly (dry locks would be happier with Tress). Now flop on the bed for ten relaxing minutes, at the same time beauty-treating your eyes with Optrex Eye Compresses. Next step—your feet! A massage with Dr. Scholl's Foot Cream and they'll stand up to the most reckless Rock 'n' Roll. Make-up time follows and don't forget shoulders and arms if you're wearing a low-cut dress. Leichner's Eau de Soie will give a satin finish here. Time now to put on your party dress but cover your face with a chiffon scarf to be sure your make-up stays intact. Then transfer the scarf to your shoulders and comb out your set. A spray of lacquer on your hair, perfume on pulse points, at neck and in the crook of your arm—and you're ready. Make sure your bag is, too, by a swift check of the contents. Off you go—have a lovely time!

WICKER PONY-CHAIRS.

Then they drove off in style.

Cinderella, left alone, cried bitterly.

Suddenly her fairy godmother appeared.

In a flash she changed Cinderella's rags
into cloth of gold.

She touched a pumpkin
with her wand

She gave her a pair of glass slippers

and it turned into a carriage.

'But remember the time.'

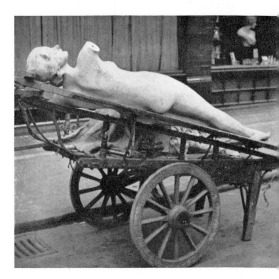

or your finery will all turn to rags.'

Cinderella promised
to be home by twelve o'clock and set

'Leave by midnight,

in her handsome carriage in high spirit

The prince danced
with her the whole evening.

When midnight approached,

Cinderella told him they must part

and she drove
swiftly away.

The next night there was another ball.

Frying To-night

The prince did not

leave Cinderella for an instant.

He paid her such compliments

that she was tempted
to forget the time.

All of a sudden it struck twelve.

As Cinderella ran off   her ball-dress vanished,

and her coach disintegrated.

The prince tore after her.

Alas, he found no trace of her but a little glass slipper.

A herald announced   that the girl whose foot the slipper would fit

was to marry the prince.

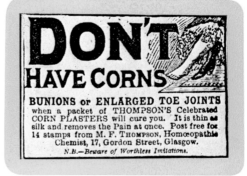

All the ladies of the town, the sisters too,

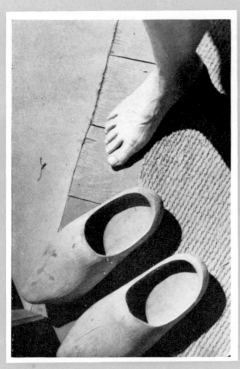

tried on the slipper.

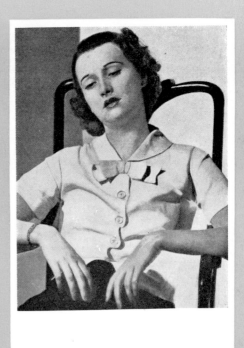

But in vain.

When Cinderella said she would try,

the sisters burst out laughing.

But it fitted to a T.

The fairy godmother appeared.

At a touch

Cinderella was transformed

The sisters were terrified   and overcome with confusion.

Cinderella and the prince were united.

It was a perfect match.